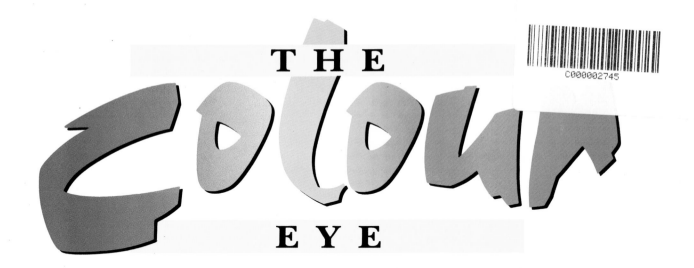

THE Colour EYE

ROBERT CUMMING & TOM PORTER

BBC BOOKS

This book accompanies the BBC TV series *The Colour Eye*,
first broadcast on BBC2 from August 1990. The series
was produced by Suzanne Davies and Julian Stenhouse, and
prepared in consultation with the Continuing Education
Advisory Council
Published by BBC Books,
a division of BBC Enterprises Limited,
Woodlands, 80 Wood Lane, London W12 0TT
First published 1990
© Robert Cumming and Tom Porter 1990
ISBN 0 563 21528 3
Illustrations by Danny McBride
Set in $11/12\frac{1}{2}$ pt Baskerville and
printed and bound in Great Britain by
Butler & Tanner Ltd, Frome and London
Colour separations by Technik Limited, Berkhamsted
Cover printed by Clays Ltd, St Ives plc

PICTURE CREDITS

BIBLIOGRAPHY

BIRREN, F. *Color and human response* New York: Van Nostrand Reinhold, pbk., 1984

BIRREN, F. *History of color in painting* New York: Van Nostrand Reinhold, 1965. op.

BIRREN, F. *Light, color and environment* New York: Van Nostrand Reinhold, pbk., 1982

DE GRANDIS, L. *Theory and use of colour* Blandford, 1986. op.

EISEMAN, L. ed. *Color News* Vol. 2 no. 1, March, 1987; Vol. 3 no. 4, March, 1988; Vol. 4 no. 2, June, 1989; Vol. 4 no. 3, October 1989

FAVRE, J.P. and NOVEMBER, A. *Color and communication* Zurich: ABC Editions, 1978. op.

GETTENS, R.J. and STOUT, G.L. *Painting materials* New York: Dover, new edn., pbk., 1966

ITTEN, J. *Elements of color* New York: Van Nostrand Reinhold, new edn., pbk., 1983

JACKSON, C. *Colour me beautiful* Piatkus, new edn., pbk., 1983

JACKSON, C. *Colour me beautiful make-up book* Piatkus, new edn., pbk., 1983

JACQUES, B. *Colour and style file* Piatkus, 1989

LAVER, J. *Modesty in dress: an inquiry into the fundamentals of fashion* Heinemann, 1969. op.

LENCLOS, J.P. *The geography of colour* Tokyo: San'ei Shobo Pub. Co., 1989

LÜSCHER, M. *The Lüscher colour test* Pan, new edn., 1987

OSBORNE, R. *Lights and pigments* J. Murray, 1980. op.

PORTER, T. and MIKELLIDES, B. *Colour for architecture* Studio Vista, 1976. op.

PORTER, T. *Colour outside* Architectural Press, 1982. op.

PORTER, T. 'An investigation into colour preferences' in *Designer* September, 1973.

PORTER, T. *Tie Rack report* (as consultant) Munro & Forster, 1989

RHODES, Z. and KNIGHT, A. *The art of Zandra Rhodes* Cape, 1984

RILEY, B. *Working with colour* Arts Council of Great Britain, pbk., 1984

ROUTLEDGE, P. 'Food workers' in *Observer* 29 October 1989

SLOANE, P. *Colour: basic principles, new directions* Studio Vista, 1969. op.

TAYLOR, F. *Colour technology for artists, craftsmen and industrial designers* Oxford U.P., 1962. op.

VARLEY, H. ed. *Colour* Mitchell Beazley, 1980

WAGNER, C. *The Wagner colour response report* Chicago: Wagner Institute for colour research, 1985

ZELANSKI, P. and M. P. FISHER *Colour: for designers and artists* Herbert Press, pbk., 1989

Paint and painting: an exhibition and working studio sponsored by Winsor & Newton to celebrate their 150th Anniversary London: Tate Gallery, pbk., 1982. op.

Contents

FOREWORD

The Colour Eye is for anyone with a general interest in colour and for the student who needs to study the ground rules. We have planned the book so that the different topics are presented in a logical sequence, starting with the more theoretical and abstract subjects, and then discussing how these are applied in practice. Some readers may wish to tackle the subject in the order in which we have presented it, but others may prefer to dip in and read the sections in a different sequence, and the book can be used in either way.

We hope we will help the reader to open his or her eyes to colour, and to ask questions about it; to make more informed decisions about colour, to realise how much we are affected by it in our everyday lives, and to discuss colour with other people.

Robert Cumming
Tom Porter

INTRODUCTION

Colour exerts a very strong influence on our lives. It affects the way we see, the way we feel, and the way we act. It forms part of the structure of every society. Have you ever wondered, for instance, why male babies were traditionally dressed in blue, and little girls in pink, or why danger signs are red or yellow? Everyday speech is full of references to colour. We go red as a beetroot, yellow with cowardice, green with envy, blue with cold, purple with rage, white as a sheet, and black with despair.

From the very earliest times colours have been connected with emotion, magic and religion, and have been given symbolic and subjective meanings. Scientists, doctors and psychologists have, for years, investigated the psychology of colour and attempted to understand more fully why we react differently to different colours, and to examine if there are any general rules and principles behind our reactions.

Most of us have quite strong preferences about colour. They may be quite specific – a liking for red ties, for example. Or we may prefer a particular colour group, for example, the fresh sharp

TOP AND BOTTOM: *the structure of every*
Colour forms part of *society.*

There are endless opportunities for experimenting with colour: clothes, make-up, rooms, gardens, food. If you need inspiration, think of the beautiful and subtle colours of a simple soap bubble.

colours of spring or the warm mellow tones of autumn. Detailed and extensive studies on colour preference and the psychology of colours have been carried out since the 1930s and 1940s. The results are not always scientific, but they produce useful anecdotal evidence which furthers our understanding of colour and which anyone can experiment with or use. Colour preference tests using cards and a questionnaire can easily be organised amongst a group of friends, and students can be encouraged to carry out a general survey. The famous Lüscher Colour Test is discussed on page 106.

Some experiments do produce factual

results. For instance, in one famous experiment, factory productivity was increased significantly when the wash rooms were painted an unattractive shade of green – the workforce went back to work rather than linger in them. In another factory there were complaints that boxes which were coloured dark blue were too heavy to carry. When the same boxes were coloured yellow the complaints ceased.

Advertisers and companies are, of course, very aware of the suggestive power of colour (see page 136), and one's own experience and common sense suggests that each colour has its own individual characteristics and associations. In fact, there seems to be a wide range of agreement as to what these are and the evidence from myths and symbolism across an extensive range of history and societies shows how universal much of this agreement has been.

Black cats have always been thought to have mysterious powers. Sometimes they have been seen as evil, sometimes as a sign of good luck. Most domestic animals are thought to be colour blind.

LIGHT AND THE SPECTRUM

Newton analysed the composition of light. In a darkened room he shone a thin beam of daylight through a triangular glass prism. The prism broke up the beam of daylight into the colours of the spectrum, from red to violet, and he was able to project these onto a screen. Furthermore, the sequence of the colours remained constant – red, orange, yellow, green, blue, violet. Newton named a seventh colour between blue and violet which he called indigo, a rich dark blue colour. Today it is customary to identify only the six colours listed above. Like many men of his century, Newton had a mystical side to his nature, and he had a strong wish to identify seven colours, seven being an important 'magic' number. He allied his seven colours to the seven spheres, and to the seven notes on the musical scale.

Newton's discovery was not, in itself, new; the light spectrum is one of the most beautiful phenomena seen in nature. Raindrops act like individual prisms to break up daylight, and the resulting effect is a rainbow. But Newton then went on to do something new. Using another prism he reunited the broken up beam of daylight to make another thin beam of daylight. In other words he showed that white light is composed of the colours of the spectrum, and that there is a reversible process in which it can be broken up and then recomposed.

Many experiments to try to discover what light is were carried out in the 19th century. In 1860 James Clerk Maxwell showed that light was a form of electromagnetic energy. Just as a radio can receive electromagnetic energy of certain frequencies and turn them into sound, the eye is able to receive light waves between 400 million million cycles per second, and 800 million million cycles per second, and we perceive them as colour, violet being the shortest wavelength and red the longest.

Einstein's investigations at the beginning of this century showed that light behaved in a much more complex way than had previously been thought. The

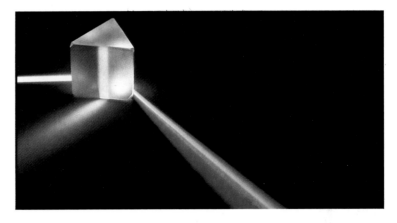

ABOVE: *White light passing through a triangular prism, which splits the light into spectral colours.*
FAR LEFT: *In the rainbow, nature reveals all the colours of the spectrum.*

question 'What is light?' has yet to receive a definitive answer.

The range and order of the colours are easy to remember through the following mnemonic: 'Richard of York gave battle in vain'. The first letter of each word corresponds to the name and place of the colours in the spectrum. This includes indigo.

WAVELENGTH

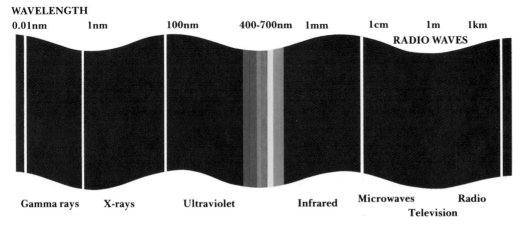

| 0.01nm | 1nm | 100nm | 400-700nm | 1mm | 1cm | 1m | 1km |

RADIO WAVES

Gamma rays   **X-rays**   **Ultraviolet**   **Infrared**   **Microwaves**   **Radio**
Television

LEFT: *This diagram shows the place of light in the electromagnetic spectrum. The wavelengths of electromagnetic radiations are measured in metric units. One nanometre = one thousand-millionths of a metre.*

THE COLOUR WHEEL

The colour wheel is one of the basic tools used in the analysis and discussion of colour. Originally devised by Newton, there have been many variations of it, although the basic principle remains the same. All the colours of the spectrum are contained in the wheel in the correct sequence. By adding purple, which is a mixture of red and blue, the colours can be placed in the form of a circle.

The colour wheel shown here is the one devised by Johannes Itten in the middle of this century. His purpose was to create an easily remembered diagram with twelve hues that could be clearly visualised, which would enable intermediate hues to be quickly located, and which would provide an orderly, logical and objective basis for working with colour pigments or paints.

In the triangle in the centre are the three primary colours, yellow, blue and red. They are called primaries because they cannot be created by the mixture of other pigments. Alongside them, in the shape of flat triangles, are the three secondary colours which are produced by mixing the primaries according to Itten's scheme. Thus, blue and yellow produces green; red and yellow produces orange; red and blue produces violet. Around these triangles is the colour wheel,

divided into twelve sectors. Six of these are filled by the primaries and the secondaries, and between each primary and secondary there is another colour. Itten called these tertiary colours, each tertiary being obtained by the mixture of a primary and a secondary. Thus, yellow and orange produces yellow-orange; red and orange produces red-orange; yellow and green produces yellow-green; and so on. It would be possible to create further subdivisions, but Itten considered this to be unnecessary.

Mixing coloured lights does not produce the same result as mixing colour pigments. This is explained on page 34.

Itten was interested in colour from a scientific and spiritual viewpoint. He taught at the famous Bauhaus School in Germany in the 1920s and the elements of the Bauhaus course, including the colour wheel, have become a standard feature of art instruction throughout the world. His most famous book, *The Art of Colour*, was published in 1961.

RIGHT: *Itten's colour wheel.*

THE LANGUAGE OF COLOUR

The language we use to describe colour is often imprecise. We talk about the colour red, for example, but there are bluey reds, yellowy reds, pale reds and dark reds. It is important, therefore, to establish a practical basic vocabulary in order to explain more accurately what we see and what we mean. The diagram on page 15 should help to make things clearer.

Hue

The word hue is what is commonly thought of as colour. A particular red is of a specific hue, for example. On the accompanying diagram there are twelve different hues, from violet in the second left column to purple at the right. It would be possible to produce a much larger chart with additional hues added between those shown here. It is estimated that normal vision can differentiate approximately ten million different hues, and practice does make the eye sharper.

Saturation

Saturation describes the purity of a specific hue. Other words to describe saturation are colourfulness, chroma, intensity, weight and purity. In the diagram on page 15 there is one square for each hue which represents that hue at full saturation. Yellow at full saturation is

RIGHT: The twelve hues of the colour circle in matching tonal values or brilliancies.

on the third line, red on the sixth and blue on the eighth (see below).

Tone

Other words to describe tone are lightness, value, brilliance, greyness and luminosity. Towards the top of the diagram each hue is progressively diluted with white, and towards the bottom it is progressively darkened with black. The far left column shows 12 equidistant steps from grey to black. Each line, reading from left to right, shows hues of equal tonal value. Yellow stands out immediately. Fully saturated yellow has the brightest tone of the hues. Saturated red is in the middle of the diagram and needs diluting with white to reach the equivalent tonal value of yellow. Saturated blue is nearer the bottom of the diagram and needs more dilution with white than red does to reach the equivalent yellow tonal value. The diagram also shows hues working together in relationships, and demonstrates how a saturated hue stands out amongst less saturated colours, and how a hue of different tone would stand out in a group where the others were of equal tonal value. Understanding colour relationships, and choosing the right saturation and tone, is as important as choosing the right hue.

Colour Symbolism and Psychology: *Red*

ა შეუბრძოლის კავკასიელ
ხალხთა ძმობას!

Да здравствует братство
всех народов Кавказа!

Н. Кочергин. Тифлис   N. Kotsherguin. Tiflis

Red has many variations. Warm orange reds are, by their nature, earthy and physical, whereas cool purply reds have a character which is mysterious and magical. Reds can be bright or dark, dull or clear, but the essential and strong character of the hue is never lost in these many variations.

Symbolism

Red is the colour of fire and passion. It suggests activity, love, joy, energy, strength, assertiveness, ferocity and fertility. It can also imply evil and disaster. It is, after all, the colour of the devil. Most cultures associate red with fire.

In ancient Egypt red was the colour of the sun god Ra. In Greek and Roman mythology it represented the goddess of agriculture, Ceres, who was often shown holding up a torch. Dionysus or Bacchus, the god of wine, is frequently depicted with a red face. It was also the colour of Mars, the god of war. Red is the Chinese marriage colour, and in heraldry it symbolises courage and zeal.

For the American Indians red is the colour of the desert and disaster, and in Celtic symbolism it suggests death and calamity. For Christians red symbolises the blood of Christ, martyrdom and cruelty, and is the colour of the robes of cardinals who are the soldiers of the Pope. Saints' days are written in red lettering in the church calendar, and so we have the phrase 'red letter day' to denote a special occasion.

Red is often the colour of revolutionary and violent change, and was the symbolic colour of the French Revolution.

Psychology

In colour preference tests, red and blue stand out as the most commonly preferred colours (see pages 150–1). However, a dislike of red is also fairly common, and is explained by psychologists as a characteristic of someone who has been frustrated or defeated. Pink, which is red diluted with white, is thought to be the preference of someone who lacks the courage to favour red, and who seeks tenderness, affection and gentility.

Exposure to red causes measurable reactions in the body. Blood pressure goes up, breathing and pulse rates quicken, sweating begins and brain waves are stimulated. However, the effects are only temporary and soon die down again. Red-orange light promotes vegetable growth and organic function. In dark conditions, the eye is at its sharpest under red light, which is why there is often red illumination in aircraft control rooms and similar environments.

LEFT AND ABOVE: *Variations of red are found in a host of objects both man-made and natural; from a poster from the Russian Revolution to ripe strawberries.*

Orange

Orange is the colour of warmth, fruit and flowers, and of the luscious, strong tasting and strong scented orange. It is a colour which is vividly present in sunsets (although rarely in sunrises), and is much in evidence in late summer and autumn when fruit ripens and the leaves turn. It is seen most widely and in most variety in nature.

Symbolism

In Greek mythology orange was the colour of Jupiter, the supreme ruler of the gods and mortals, and the chief of the twelve gods who lived on Mount Olympus. The robes of Buddhist monks are coloured saffron to symbolise humility. For the Chinese and Japanese orange is the colour of love and happiness. In heraldry orange symbolises strength and endurance. Some pictures illustrating the temptation in the Garden of Eden show Eve giving Adam an orange rather than an apple from the Tree of Knowledge.

Psychology

People who favour orange are said to be cheerful with a ready smile, quick witted, talkative, to like company and desire action. Other commentators, however, have said that orange may also be picked

ABOVE: *Nature uses orange in rich variety.*

RIGHT: *Buddhist monks wear saffron robes to symbolise humility.*

by those who suffer from physical and mental exhaustion. Perhaps they choose the colour as a wish fulfilment to compensate for the vitality which they lack. Small children favour warm luminous colours such as red, orange, pink and yellow.

Researchers have claimed that an orange environment improves social behaviour, cheers the spirit and lessens hostility and irritability. However, professional designers and decorators seldom create orange environments and you do not see many orange bedrooms and sitting rooms. Intense orange is striking, but it is not a very flexible colour for use in decorating. Orange diluted with white soon loses its character, and mixed with black it declines into an unexciting brown.

There is often disagreement as to whether an object is coloured orange or a variation of red or yellow. Red and yellow are colours with stronger characters and wider associations.

Orange is a colour which stands out strongly and so is often used in factories to indicate acute hazards such as cutting edges, gears, pulleys, hot pipes and exposed wires, and in trains to show moving doors.

Yellow

There are many beautiful poetical and literary allusions to yellow corn and yellow hair, and yellow and gold are often linked together both visually and in the imagination.

Symbolism

Among the heavenly spheres, each of which has its own colour, yellow is the symbolic colour of the sun. For the ancient Greeks it represented fire and the sun, and for Hindus and Christians it symbolises life and truth. For the Chinese and Leonardo da Vinci it was the colour of the earth. It is the Hindu marriage colour, and was the colour of Athena the classical goddess of wisdom and the patroness of institutions of learning and the arts. In heraldry it designated honour and loyalty.

Yellow can also suggest negative characteristics. Dark yellow has been used to indicate treason and jealousy, and yellow has often been the symbol of cowardice, prejudice and persecution. Judas Iscariot is often portrayed in pictures wearing a yellow robe.

Psychology

Yellow is said to be selected by people who are intelligent, who like innovation, have great hopes and expectations and seek happiness. It is thought to be avoided by people who have suffered disappointments, and who, consequently, have a tendency to be isolated and suspicious. On the other hand, it has been noted that yellow is a colour which is well liked by the mentally handicapped (see also pages 102–3 and 106–7).

Yellow is the brightest portion of the spectrum, and yellow and black is the most intense of all the colour combinations. In industrial safety codes yellow usually indicates hazards such as low beams, obstructions and moving equipment such as cranes and fork lift trucks. Ships show a yellow, or yellow and black flag to indicate they are in quarantine.

LEFT: *The bright yellow of flowering rape dramatically changes the balance and mood of the English countryside.*

BELOW: *The yellow and black of this wasp are warning signs to predators.*

Green

Green is a very flexible hue with many variations and associations. The addition of yellow gives yellow-greens with their implication of spring, early growth and youth. The addition of blue gives blue-greens which are suggestive of ice and cold. The addition of red and orange gives a wide range of dark greens which can be wonderfully rich and mysterious, suggestive of dark, damp hidden places, or brown-greens which are the colours of late summer and early autumn.

Symbolism

Green is the colour of the vegetable kingdom, and symbolically it is used to imply the natural world, and hope. The connection between the two is clear, for the regeneration of nature and the growth of fresh green seedlings out of apparently barren earth is a potent image that has been used by all societies. Thus in Egyptian buildings the floors were often painted green and the ceilings blue. The Chinese used green to symbolise wood, whereas Leonardo da Vinci used it to symbolise water. St John the Divine gave Christ the colour emerald green and in medieval times green was the colour of the Trinity and St John the Evangelist. For the ancient Greeks green was the colour of Venus. Venus was the

LEFT: *Green is the colour of growth, and the symbolic colour for fertility and hope.*

RIGHT: *A tree frog shows that green is capable of many subtle variations in hue.*

goddess of love and fertility, and her sacred plant was the myrtle, an evergreen shrub which symbolised everlasting love, and marital fidelity in particular. In the Christian Church green vestments symbolise the hope of eternal life, and in heraldry green is the symbol of growth and hope. Green is the sacred colour of Islam.

Psychology

In industrial safety codes it indicates first aid devices, stretcherboxes and safety controls. In shipping a green flag indicates a wreck at sea.

Adults who prefer green are said to be well adjusted, civilised and conventional people. Children who choose green are said to be well balanced and without strong overt emotions. On the other hand we describe someone as 'green' if they are inexperienced or naive. This is probably an association with the green of fresh, young growth. A rejection of green is said to indicate a degree of mental disturbance, and a complex lonely existence. A liking for blue-green is said to indicate self-love and self-centredness (see also pages 102–3 and 106–7).

Green surroundings are thought to be good for meditation, and to encourage a purposeful state of mind which seeks an exact fulfilment of the task in hand.

Blue

Blue is very much the hue of the sky and the sea, both of which can vary from the palest ethereal shades to the deepest blue-black. The sky and the sea imply vast and infinite spaces, stretching to the far horizon; dark unfathomable depths; and the unending reaches of the universe. Although capable of great variation, blue is always cool, and as it gets blacker it implies darkness and night and the absence of light.

Symbolism

Blue is often used to symbolise authority and spirituality. In the Old Testament it is the colour of God the Father, and in the New Testament it is the colour of the Virgin Mary. In heraldry blue symbolises piety and sincerity. In Greek and Roman mythology blue was the symbolic colour of the sky gods Jupiter and Juno, and of Mercury, the winged messenger of the gods. Blue has often been used to imply heaven, truth, eternity, faith, peace, loyalty, chastity, prudence, wisdom and contemplation.

The flag of the European Community shows gold stars on a blue background.

Psychology

Colour preference tests (see pages 150–1) frequently show blue as the first choice.

People who prefer blue are said to be conservative, accomplished, deliberate and successful. They know how to earn money, and make the right connections. A rejection of blue indicates anxiety, a fear of loss of wealth and status, and a sense of failure. A preference for blue also indicates a desire for order and peace, and an inner wish for a benign life (see also pages 102–3 and 106–7).

Tests have shown that exposure to blue has a calming influence. Blood pressure, pulse rate and brain waves slow down – an effect which is also noticeable with exposure to purple and violet. Blue is not an easy colour for the eye to focus on, and in blue light objects appear blurred and surrounded by haloes. In industrial safety codes blue is used to mark equipment that may not be used without permission, and for electrical equipment such as motors and generators.

RIGHT: *Blue; heaven, peace, truth, contemplation.*

Violet and purple

A Catholic priest celebrating mass wearing symbolic purple vestments.

Violet is the colour with the shortest wavelength in the spectrum. Beyond it lies ultra-violet which the human eye cannot see, but which can be detected by many insects. Insects have a different range of colour vision to humans and

birds as they are more attracted to the shorter wavelengths such as violet and ultra-violet. They may not be able to detect, or may be repelled by, the longer wavelengths such as red. Thus, red flowers which are attractive to humans may not be so to some insects. Some flowers have developed so that they will reflect ultra-violet light and so be notice-able to insects. The patterns on the wings of some moths and butterflies will appear different when seen under ultra-violet light from the patterns seen under day-light.

Symbolism

Symbolically violet is the colour of Mary Magdalene and Jupiter, and has been used to indicate knowledge, sanctity, humility, sorrow, nostalgia and old age.

Purple is closely related to violet. Purple is a mixture of blue and red in the same way that green is a mixture of blue and yellow. Purple is a particularly rich colour, and carries with it suggestions of wealth and extravagance. In heraldry it denotes rank and royalty, and purple robes have been habitually worn by kings and emperors. The word purple comes from the name of a shellfish which yielded a very expensive coloured dye that was used for the robes of Roman emperors and magistrates. The Byzantine imperial family wrapped their new born children in purple robes, from which we get the phrase 'born in the purple' to indicate particularly favourable circumstances of birth. Purple vestments are often worn for Christian baptisms, and for Lent and Advent.

Psychology

In colour preference tests violet ranks over yellow and orange, but below red, blue and green (see pages 150–1). Those who prefer violet are said to be sensitive and tasteful, with a liking for arts, philosophy, music and ballet. They are temperamental with high ideals, and may be seeking enchantment or a magical state in which their innermost wishes are fulfilled. People who dislike violet are said by some to be people who hate pretence, conceit and vanity, and by others to be people who avoid close relationships (see pages 102–3 and 106–7).

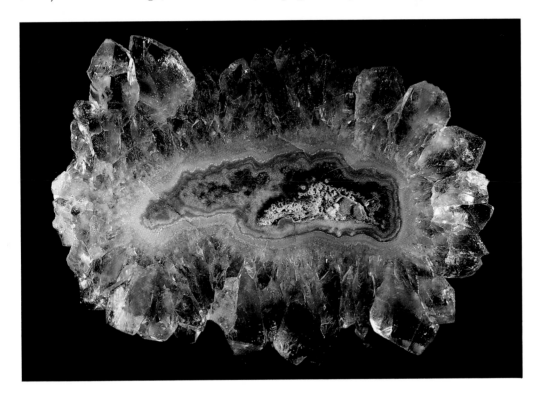

The vivid purple of an amethyst.

Black and grey

ABOVE: *Black and grey is the colour worn by modern business and bureaucracy, and the colour of many urban environments.*

RIGHT: *Goya's* Witches' Gathering *(detail).*

Black implies the extinction of all light and colour. Without light there is no life, and true black is rarely found in living nature. When we describe a colour in nature as black it will normally be found, on close examination, to be a very dark variation of another colour, in the same way that white is normally a very pale version of another colour. Even the darkest material, which we perceive as black, reflects at least three per cent of the light falling on it, which means that colour must be present. There are no natural black flowers in nature. Those that are available have been artificially bred, and are very dark variants of

another colour. Where black does appear in nature – as in coal and crude oil – it tends to be the colour of dead and decomposed matter.

Neutral grey is obtained when all spectral wavelengths are absorbed to the same degree. Grey may be mixed from black and white, or from any pair of complementary colours, provided they are the exact complementaries. Thus red and green, violet and yellow, blue and orange, will mix to form neutral grey. Grey is rarely found in nature, where it is usually a variation or blend of one colour.

Symbolism

Among Western civilisations black is almost universally the colour of death and mourning, and in the symbolism of heraldry it signifies grief and penitence. For the Irish and the Chinese black was the colour of the north, almost certainly because the northern sky represented night. Black is the symbolic colour of the god Saturn, the Roman god of agriculture. His festival in December was the origin of our Christmas. Black cats were sacred to the Egyptians and in Europe a black cat which crosses your path is a sign of good luck. In the United States, however, it signifies bad luck. By and large the symbolism of black is negative. It is the colour of witches, of evil, and disaster. We talk about black magic, black Monday, the black sheep of the family, a *bête noire*, and black lies.

Psychology

In colour preference tests black is rarely selected, and is often actively disliked. It is said to be chosen by people who may be fighting against fate. Black has often been the colour worn by those who are in open revolt against society, such as the anarchists of the 19th century and the beatniks of the 1950s (see page 107). Yet black and grey are colours which are frequently worn, especially for official functions and in the world of business. The reason may be that black and grey tend to obscure individuality, and on such occasions the conscious or unconscious aim may be to be anonymous, in the sense of conforming and appearing respectable, and not standing out as different (see pages 128–9).

Grey suggests a world of shadows and shadowy appearances, asking to be enlivened by a flash of colour. An *éminence grise* is the powerful but unseen and generally unknown person who influences events, whilst the colourful personality of the monarch or leading politician attracts attention.

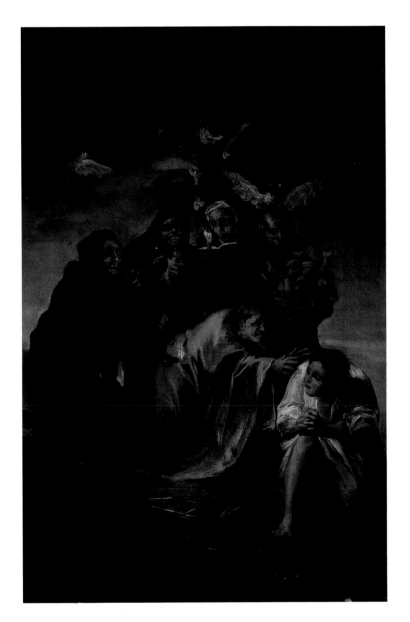

White

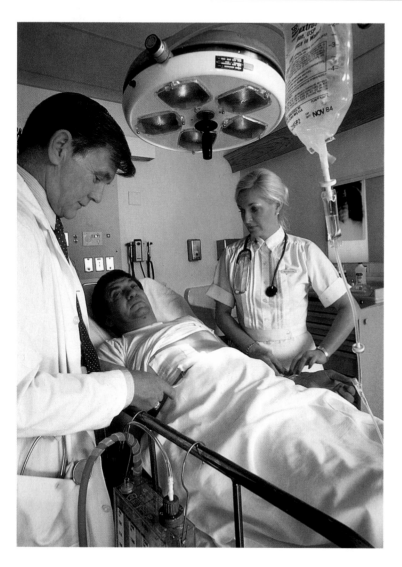

White does not have the strong links and associations of other colours. It is a colour which stands on its own. A snowy winter landscape has a strange and unreal quality to it. It is not permanent, and it suggests the absence of the natural colours of earth and foliage. It is this quality that makes white the natural colour of purity and innocence. Equally it makes it the natural background on which or with which other colours play their part visually and emotionally.

Is white a colour? It is a question which is often asked, and often answered in the negative. It would, however, defy common sense and our use of everyday language to say that it is not a colour. Leonardo da Vinci answered the question in the following way. Writing nearly five hundred years ago, his comments remain remarkably perceptive and shrewd. 'The first of all simple colours is white, though philosophers will not acknowledge white or black to be colours; because the first is the cause or the receiver of colours, and the other totally deprived of them. But as painters cannot do without either, we shall place them among the others; and according to this order of things, white will be the first, yellow the second, green the third, blue the fourth, red the fifth, and black

the sixth. We shall set down white for the representation of light, without which no colour can be seen; yellow for the earth; green for water; blue for air; red for fire; and black for total darkness.'

Symbolism

In the symbolism of the heavenly spheres white is the colour for the moon and in Western societies it is associated with innocence, purity, joy and glory. It is the

ABOVE: *The absence of natural colours makes a winter landscape seem unreal.*

LEFT: *In hospitals, the cleanliness suggested by white is now sometimes replaced with 'friendlier' colours.*

traditional colour for christenings and weddings. In Imperial Rome and Nationalist China, however, white, not black, was the appropriate colour for death and mourning. The Chinese wore white as an acknowledgement that the deceased had left the earth for a new purer spiritual state. In heraldry white symbolises faith and purity. For the Hindus and the Greeks white was the colour for water.

SEEING COLOUR

The eye is constantly experiencing a dazzling variety of coloured objects and coloured light. The natural world is full of colour which can be of great intensity or intriguing subtlety. If you look closely at the petals of a rose, the feathers of a bird or the scales of a fish you will see miracles of different colour. If you spend an hour looking at the sky in early morning or late evening you can see astonishing sequences of changing colour.

Our perception of colour is a complex interaction between the eye and the brain which is not fully understood. The eye is receptive to light, just as the ear is receptive to sound waves, and it converts this stimulus into an impulse which is sent to the brain. Sometimes the eye, or the link between the eye and the brain, does not work properly, resulting in colour blindness. Eight per cent of men and one per cent of women cannot tell the difference between red, green and grey (see tests on page 36).

Between them the eye and the brain can be highly subjective and selective. Sometimes we cannot see what is there, and at other times we see what is not there. Some people experience colour sensations when hearing sounds (this is called synaesthesia – see page 91) and blind people can sometimes feel colours, and differentiate between them with their hands. It is worth experimenting with touch and sound to see if you can extend and develop the way in which you 'see' and experience colour. What we taste is also closely linked to what we see.

In the last two hundred years, as we have developed from an agricultural into an industrial society, we have discovered the means of making new colouring substances – pigments and dyes – with which to decorate ourselves and our environment. Although we now have the means to stimulate the eye and mind with colour and to brighten our industrial environment with lights, the dominant colour of the modern man-made urban and industrial environment seems, sadly, to be grey. Concrete, cement, machinery, working dress and artificial light have none of the variety and changing colours of natural light. Much of what we see in colour is the result of recent technological developments. Fifty years ago colour films, television and inexpensive colour printing and packaging were all at an experimental stage, and lasers were an idea which had yet to be developed. Today we probably take all of them for granted, yet if they were taken away our lives would be considerably less colourful, pleasurable and convenient.

Peacock feathers are famous for their deep and lustrous colours.

Mixing colours

Mixing coloured lights and mixing coloured pigments produces very different results. If coloured lights are mixed together the resulting colour corresponds to the combined wavelengths of the lights which are mixed. Thus if all the colours are combined together as light, the product will be white light, because white light contains all the colours of the spectrum. We call the colours so formed **additive colours** and they are created by **additive colour mixing**.

Pigments, on the other hand, absorb light wavelengths. Thus a pure red pigment would absorb all light wavelengths other than red. In practice pigments are never pure. For example, yellow and blue pigments reflect a little of some other colours. When yellow and a certain blue are combined they create green because green is the one colour which is reflected by both of them. Since they absorb light, colour pigments look less bright than coloured lights, and the more they are mixed together the duller they get, because they increasingly absorb more light. If all colours are mixed together as pigments they should, in theory, create black because all light wavelengths should be absorbed. In practice, because pigments are never pure, they combine to produce a brownish grey rather than black. Colours which are created by pigments are called **subtractive colours**, and are produced by **subtractive colour mixing**.

Coloured lights

Diagram A shows the three primary colours of light: green, blue and red. The effect of the diagram can be recreated by projecting three beams of light onto a screen through three filters of these primary colours. Only rays of the same colour as the filter will pass through. They are called primaries because they cannot be produced by mixing other coloured lights. Where they overlap they mix to create secondary colours, and these are magenta (bluish red), cyan (greenish blue) and yellow. If all three primary colours are mixed together white light is produced. Also, if blue light and yellow are mixed together white light will be produced, yellow being a mixture of the other two primaries, red and green. Blue and yellow are complementary colours because together they produce white light; red and cyan, and green and magenta are also complementary colours. By mixing the three primary colours in differing amounts any colour of the spectrum can be created.

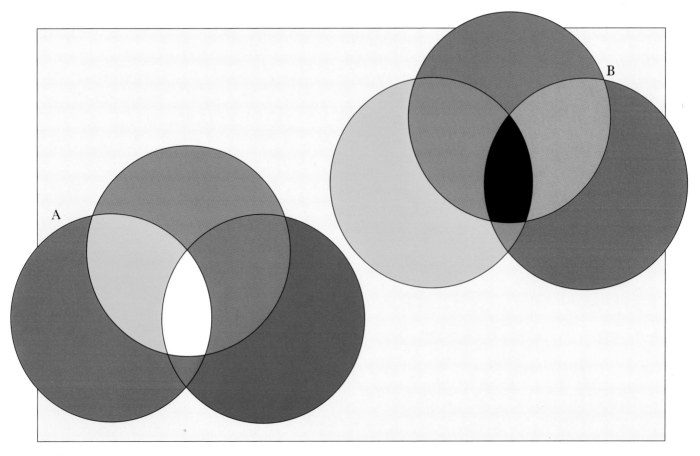

Coloured pigments

Diagram B shows the three traditional primary pigment colours. They are red, blue and yellow. They are called primaries because they cannot be created by mixing other pigment colours. If they are pure colours they will combine to produce black. Blue and yellow combine to form green which is the complementary of red, and red and green combine to make black, according to traditional colour theory. Similarly, blue and orange (which is a mixture of red and yellow) are complementaries; and yellow and violet (which is a mixture of red and blue) are complementaries (see also pages 12–13).

The eye

The eye works very much like a camera. There is a lens which focuses the rays of light, and an iris which controls the amount of light falling on the lens and so reaching the inside of the eye. At the back of the eyeball is the retina, a transparent lining which contains light receptors which are activated by the light falling on them. There are two kinds of light receptors, called rods and cones after their respective shapes. Cones are able to convey colour sensation, whereas rods are not. It is thought that there are three types of cones, each containing a pigment sensitive to red, blue or green – the three additive primaries. In daylight cones are active and in very dim light the eye functions principally with rods. There are approximately seven million cones and 120 million rods in each eye, with one million nerve fibres leading from the retina to the optic nerve.

The optic nerve connects the eye to the brain. There is a blind spot with no rods or cones in the middle of the retina where the optic nerve joins. Cones are concentrated in the middle of the retina near the optic nerve, whereas rods are concentrated at the edges. There is a special area of the eye called the fovea which contains only cones. It is only one millimetre in diameter but it gives the sharpest colour vision, and when we look at things in detail the eye automatically focuses the image here. At night time the centre of the eye sees very little, and objects can sometimes be seen more clearly if the eye is focused on a spot to one side of the object.

The information received by the eye is conveyed to the brain, so the perception

Someone with normal colour vision will see 5 and 8. Someone with red/green deficiency will see 3 instead of 8 and 2 instead of 5. A person with total colour blindness will see no numbers.

of colour is, therefore, a mental and psychological phenomenon as well as a physical one. It seems that the physical function of the eye is directly affected by emotions. Experiments have shown that when we see something we like the pupil opens wider to admit more light, and when we see something we do not like the reverse happens.

Yellow light naturally focuses directly onto the retina, and is the colour which we perceive most acutely. Red light nat-

urally focuses at a point behind the retina, so the lens of the eye has to grow convex to focus the red on the retina and in so doing gives the sensation of pulling the colour nearer. That is why red, when seen with other colours, seems to advance in front of them. Blue naturally focuses at a point in front of the retina, so that the lens grows concave to focus it, and gives the sensation of pushing the colour back, so blue seems to recede in comparison with other colours.

A 'cut away' illustration of a human eye.

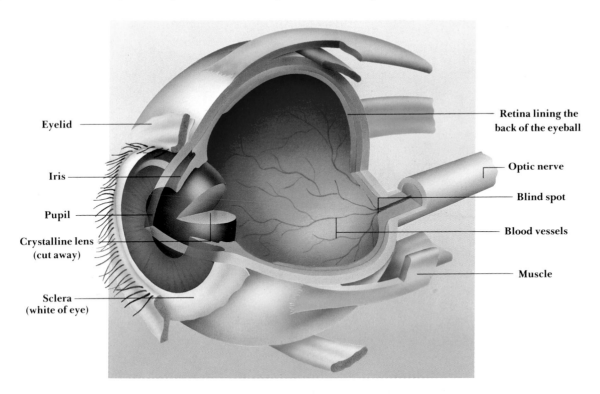

Eyelid

Iris

Pupil

Crystalline lens
(cut away)

Sclera
(white of eye)

Retina lining the
back of the eyeball

Optic nerve

Blind spot

Blood vessels

Muscle

Colour television

The principle of a colour television screen is simple, although the technology that makes it work in practice is highly sophisticated. When we look at a colour television screen we are seeing additive colour mixing in action (see pages 34–5).

The inner surface of the television tube is covered with groups of phosphor dots about $\frac{1}{2}$ millimetre in diameter which glow when struck by a beam of electrons. The dots are arranged in groups of three

(which are called triads) and they glow with the three light primary colours, red, blue and green.

In the neck of the television tube are three electron guns, each representing one of these three colours. Each gun activates the appropriate coloured phosphor dot. The current emitted by the gun can vary in strength and so alter the brightness of the glow of each dot. In most systems there is a perforated metal screen

TOP RIGHT: *The beam passes through a hole and then diverges a little between the shadow mask and the screen. Therefore, each colour meets up with its corresponding colour dot.*

BOTTOM RIGHT: *Close-up of a video screen image.*

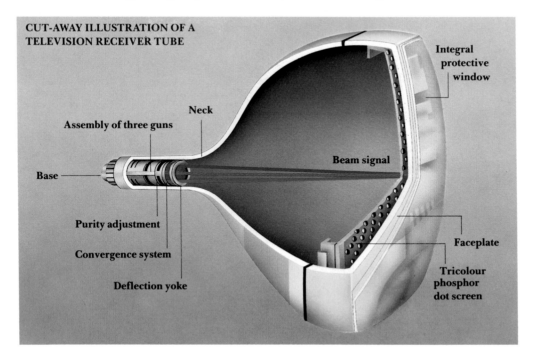

CUT-AWAY ILLUSTRATION OF A TELEVISION RECEIVER TUBE

Neck

Assembly of three guns

Base

Purity adjustment

Convergence system

Deflection yoke

Integral protective window

Beam signal

Faceplate

Tricolour phosphor dot screen

LEFT: *A 'cut away' illustration of a television receiver tube.*

called a shadow mask between the electron guns and the screen to ensure that each gun activates only the colour dot with which it is matched.

In a colour television camera the light from the scene being televised is split up into three separate versions of the scene – a red, a blue and a green version. These are then turned into an electric current which is transmitted to the television receiver and activates the three electron guns in the television tube. As well as transmitting information about hue, information about saturation and tone is also transmitted.

A television picture of a moving subject is a very rapid sequence of still pictures. Each phosphor dot glows for about $\frac{1}{50}$th of a second, and in a 20 inch television receiver there are about 400,000 triads. The electron guns in the receiver scan rapidly across the screen, from left to right and from top to bottom, much as the eye scans across a page of text when reading. In the European system the beam scans across the screen 625 times from top to bottom, and does so twenty-five times a second. The television camera scans the image which it 'sees' in exactly the same way. Human perception is not quick or precise enough to detect the gaps between the separate scans and the glowing dots, and so we have the illusion of a continuous or moving image.

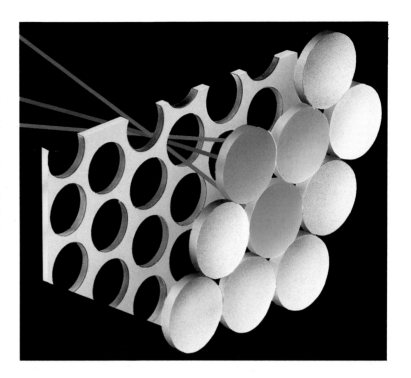

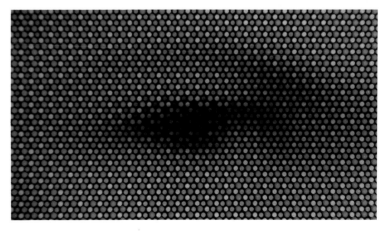

Colour printing

Most commercial and inexpensive full colour printing processes use the principle of subtractive colour mixing (see pages 34–5). Successive layers of transparent inks in the three subtractive primary colours, red (in practice, magenta), yellow and blue (in practice, cyan), are printed on a white background. These combine to create a more or less full range of colours. However, the process is not so straightforward. For example, the inks may not correspond closely enough to the exact primary colours (see page 67). Also, a dense black is not produced and a fourth printing in black often has to be added. Without black a printed image often looks too vivid and garish. Black adds definition and contrast and produces the best balance of light and dark.

For printing to take place there need to be three printable images corresponding to the three primary colours, or four images if black is to be used as a fourth printing. These images are usually produced by photography, but coloured drawings can also be used. The image to be printed in full colour is photographed onto black and white negatives three times through different colour filters – a red filter absorbs its complementary which is cyan blue; a green filter absorbs

its complementary magenta red; and a blue filter absorbs its complementary yellow. Each negative is then turned into a positive transparency which is used to print the complementary colour of the filter. Finally, the three positives are transferred onto three printing plates, which are inked with the appropriate colour. They are printed on top of each other in accurate alignment. If black is added as a fourth component, the image is photographed through a yellow filter to produce the required image.

A complete image, using the three subtractive primary colours – red, yellow and blue, as well as black.

In gravure printing variations in brightness and saturation can be obtained by varying the thickness of the transparent ink film. In other processes this variation is not possible, so the half-tone process is used. For this method, each colour separated image is broken up into a series of dots of varying size. The larger and denser the pattern of dots the more saturated the colour. Close to, therefore, the image is a network of dots of varying size in the three primary colours, plus black, plus the white of the background showing through. At normal viewing distance the eye does not see the individual dots.

The principle of full colour printing was understood in the mid 18th century, but it needed sophisticated technological developments for it to be applied in practice. The three colour process only came into its own with photography. This allowed accurate separations of the image to be made which could then be over-printed without any misalignment.

Inexpensive full colour images came into their own in the 1930s, and were fundamental to the success of mass circulation magazines. There were two reasons for this. Firstly, the development of electronic half-tone engraving machines in the 1930s enabled colour separations to be speedily and economically produced and colour corrected. Secondly there was the development of

better inks which corresponded more accurately to the three primary colours. Cheap colour packaging became popular in the 1960s thanks to the offset litho printing process, as well as the development of special inks which, in combination, allowed colour images to be printed onto almost any surface.

The three colour images required for full colour printing.

Colour photography

Modern colour film is a practical application of subtractive colour mixing (see pages 34–5). It first became available in the mid 1930s when Kodak introduced the colour slide film called Kodachrome. Called the tri-pack system, it was a way of creating an image on a flexible film, which was exposed once only through the lens of an ordinary camera, using three superimposed colour images in the primary colours – red, blue and yellow. The film was coated with three black and white emulsions, each sensitive to the three different parts of the spectrum that were required, and the three colour dyes were then added by Kodak during the processing of the film, which is why Kodachrome always has to be returned to Kodak for processing. Because the system exploits subtractive colour mixing, white is produced by shining light through clear film onto a white background and, therefore, the full colour of the transparency can be enjoyed with a relatively low source of light.

At the same time, Agfa introduced a similar colour transparency film, also using the principle of subtractive colour mixing. Agfa incorporated the colour dyes in the emulsion of the film, so that it could be processed much more simply

A positive image.

and did not have to be returned to the manufacturer. This system is the one that is used by most film manufacturers today.

Colour print film was successfully developed by Kodak during the Second World War when there was a military demand for full colour prints for aerial reconnaissance. This also uses subtractive colour mixing and three separately dyed emulsions, but in this case a colour negative is first produced. In the negative the colours which you can see are the complementaries of the colours in

the print. Thus the red element is green; the yellow element is purple, and the blue element is orange. The paper on which the print is made also has three layers of emulsion, and the three superimposed images and the transparent dyes in red, yellow and blue produce the full colour print.

The tri-pack system is ideal for colour movies. It requires a straightforward exposure through one lens, the colour separation taking place in the film emulsion. Before this development colour movies could only be produced by the Technicolor system which required very expensive and elaborate cameras and equipment. Inside the camera was a beam splitter which split the light from the lens into three beams. These were used to produce three separation negatives which were then dyed and superimposed. It was a very expensive system, but it produced superb colour. Probably the best known Technicolor movie ever produced is the epic *Gone with the Wind.*

A negative image.

43

Lasers

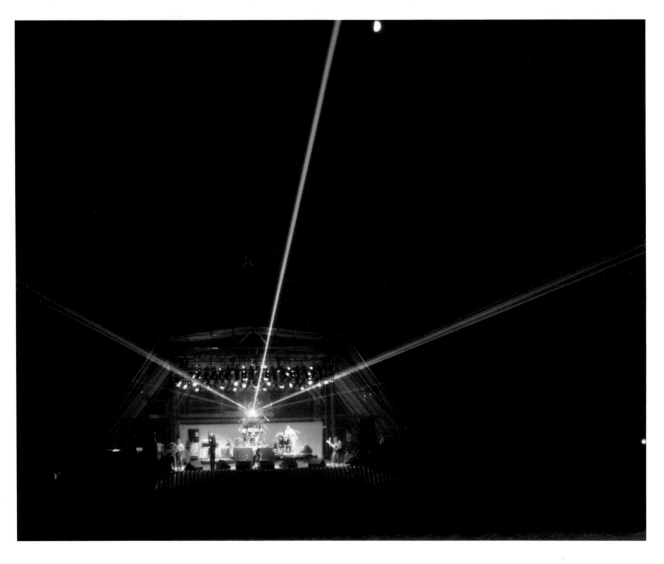

Light naturally behaves in a random and chaotic way, and is technically and rightly called 'incoherent'. Sunlight or electric light, for example, scatters a mixture of wavelengths in all directions. The significant feature of a laser is that light is made to act in a coherent fashion, and when light is made to act coherently it reaches great intensity. A laser is a razor-sharp beam of light, so dense that it can be focused on a spot no bigger than a micrometre (one millionth of a metre), and it is so intense that it will pass through a prism without being broken up. The word 'laser' is formed from the initial letters of 'Light Amplification by Stimulated Emission of Radiation' which describes how a laser beam is created.

The first laser was produced in California in 1960. Scientists used a rod of synthetic ruby which had silvered reflecting ends. One end was only partially reflective, like a two-way mirror. The atoms inside the rod were stimulated by an outside power source. This caused the atoms to emit photons of light which normally would have acted and escaped randomly. In this case, however, they could not do so, and they bounced backwards and forwards between the reflecting ends of the tube, building up to the point where they formed a regular and coherent wavelength of great intensity which was emitted through the partially silvered end of the tube. In this exper-iment with the solid rod, the light was emitted as a series of flashes. In later experiments a hollow rod filled with gas was used, and the light was emitted as a continuous beam.

Continuous beam gas lasers create a purity of hue which is unknown in nature. By using different gases a variety of hues can be obtained. Helium and neon lasers generate red and yellow light; argon generates blue and green light; krypton can be used to produce a selection of hues, most usually red; and a helium and cadmium laser emits five visible wavelengths simultaneously which combine to give white light. Recent experiments use luminescent crystals in liquid solution to produce different hues.

Lasers have been put to a wide variety of beneficial uses, notably in surgery. They are also used to create holograms, for it was not until the discovery of the laser that a bright enough source of light existed for this function. Their popular application is in laser light shows. The laser beams are so intense and dense that they look as though they have a tangible and solid quality. By using an elaborate system of prisms, filters, mirrors, and lenses, spectacular and previously unim-agined experiences of coloured light can be created.

RIGHT: *Photographs can only hint at the experience of a laser light show. Lasers can create a purity and intensity of colour unknown in nature.*

COLOUR RELATIONSHIPS

In any arrangement which uses colour, whether it is a room setting, clothes, a painting, packaging, or design, the relationships between colours is as important as the actual choice of colours.

Our response to any particular sensation can nearly always be increased by using contrasts. A sweet taste is made sweeter by contrasting it with a sour taste. Silence is more dramatic if it comes after a loud noise. A cold shower is invigorating when you are hot, whereas a hot shower is appreciated when you are cold. In the same way, our perception and response to colour is increased by the use of contrasts, that is placing one colour next to another, or using an accent of contrasting colour in an harmonious colour group.

There are no hard and fast rules about the way colour ought to be used, but a great deal can be learned by experiment and observation. One of the first people to systematically investigate colour relationships was Frenchman, Michel Eugène Chevreul (1786–1889), Director of the famous Gobelins tapestry factory. Chevreul noticed that many of the colours in his factory's tapestries looked dull when woven together, even though there was nothing wrong with the dyes. By experimenting he found that certain hues, when placed next to each other, tended to drain each other of colour. Using his observations, Chevreul worked out some basic principles of colour relationships, and published his findings in a famous book called *The Principles of Harmony and Contrast of Colours.*

The examples of colour relationships given here are similar to those that were worked out by Johannes Itten for the famous course at the Bauhaus which trained architects and designers as well as painters. He set his observations out in a series of diagrams which provide an invaluable framework, highlighting important points which are useful in all decisions about colour. On pages 108–115, there are practical suggestions for interior decoration which use the basic principles set out here.

A good example of the effects of colour relationships is shown in diagrams (A), (B), (C) and (D) on these pages. The red internal shapes never vary and the diagrams show how they appear to be significantly altered by their relationship with other hues.

(A)

(B)

Contrasts of hue

The three traditional pigment primaries, red, yellow and blue, provide the most intense example of contrasts of hue. These colours cannot be created from others, and together they make a bright, vigorous and decided contrast. If the three colours are separated by black lines their individual colour characters emerge more clearly. Useful experiments in the study of colour are – to make one (C) of the colours more dominant by using more of it; to vary the brilliance of the (D) colours and the shapes of the colours.

Three clearly differentiated hues are required to produce the most intense con- (E) trasts. The secondary colours, orange, green and violet, will produce a less dramatic contrast, and the tertiary colours a less dramatic contrast still (see the colour wheel on page 13 for secondary and tertiary colours).

The first diagram (E) shows the three primary colours, red, yellow and blue, contrasted with each other and with white and black. The second diagram (F) shows them contrasted with secondary and tertiary colours.

Complementary contrasts

The three primary pigment colours and their complementaries are red/green, yellow/violet and blue/orange. Every hue has its complementary colour. Complementary pairs have the unique charac-

(F)

teristics of balancing each other, exciting each other and, if mixed, producing a neutral grey. They also have additional peculiarities. Red and green at the same saturation have the same brilliance. Yellow and violet are an extreme light-dark contrast. Red-orange and blue-green are complementary colours which have a cold-warm contrast.

Simultaneous contrast

Simultaneous contrast is best explained by carrying out the following experiment. Take a brightly coloured sheet of paper in one of the three primary colours (red, yellow or blue). Stare hard at it for a minute, and then look at a white wall. You will 'see' a ghost-like image of the sheet of paper, but in the complementary colour. The effect is increased the longer the paper is viewed and the more lumi-(G) nous the colour. The image occurs only in the mind, and indicates that perception is(H) always seeking the complementary colour and will spontaneously create it if it is not there.

The effect can also be achieved by placing a small grey area in a field of bright colour, the grey being the same brilliance as the colour. The grey area will be perceived as being tinged with the complementary hue, and there will be a sensation of lively vibration in the grey area.

If two colours of equal brilliance,

which are not complementary, are placed together, each colour will try to shift its partner toward its own complementary, and this will alter our perception of the two colours. If the colours are well chosen they will enliven each other but if they are poorly chosen they will deaden each other. If colours of unequal brilliance are used, the effect of

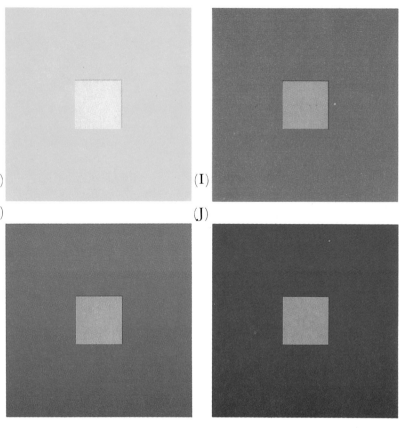

(I)

(J)

simultaneous contrast will be diminished.

In diagrams (G), (H), (I) and (J) each grey square seems to be tinged with the complementary of the background colour. To achieve the best effect the other diagrams should be covered so that only one can be seen at a time. The effect becomes stronger the longer the diagram is looked at.

Contrast of saturation

A pure intense hue can be contrasted with a less intense version of the same hue. Colours can be diluted in four ways. If diluted with varying amounts of white they become paler and colder; mixed with varying amounts of black they become darker and can change their character quite dramatically; diluted with varying amounts of grey they become dull and neutral; mixed with their complementary colour in differing proportions they produce subtle variations, and equally mixed produce a luminous grey.

Dull colours and grey can be given life by contrasting them with a saturated hue of the same tone. The dull colour must, however, be the same hue as the saturated one, or other contrasts will be introduced, which upset the harmony of the overall effect.

The grey squares in the four corners of diagram (K) are the same tone as blue. The other squares show the effect of adding differing quantities of grey to blue.

Cold-warm contrast

The hue which gives the greatest sense of warmth is red-orange, and the greatest sense of cold is given by blue-green. Experiments show that people do subjectively feel warmer in a red-orange room than in a blue-green room, even though the actual temperature is the same in both (see page 102). However cold-warm contrasts are always relative. Thus, although blues are cooler than

(K)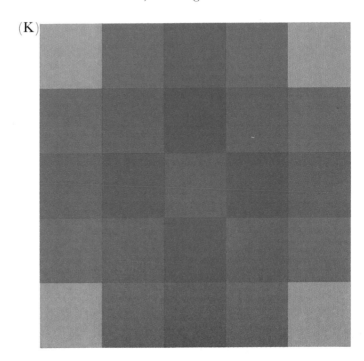

reds, some blues are warmer than others. For instance when blue is mixed with red it becomes warmer, and when it is mixed with green it becomes cooler. Equally a specific hue can appear warm if set among cool colours, but cool if set among warm colours. An accent of warm red or orange in a cool colour environment can have as dramatic an impact as a shaft of sunlight on a cold day.

The diagrams (L) and (M) show cold-warm modulations in red and green.

Light-dark contrast

Controlling light-dark relationships is one of the most difficult exercises of all. On page 15 we showed a diagram of colours which illustrates that colours at full saturation are not necessarily of the same tone. For example, saturated yellow is more brilliant than any other hue. For it to have the same tonal value as saturated blue it has to be darkened with black; to have the same tonal value as saturated yellow, blue has to be lightened with white. If saturated yellow and saturated blue are placed together there is a light-dark contrast between them.

The ability to perceive and to balance the light and dark relationships between different colours is an essential skill in all colour design. A common mistake is to render cold colours too light and warm colours too dark.

(L)

(M)

Contrast of extension

Some colours appear more dominant than others, so that only a small area of the dominant colour is needed to produce an harmonious balance with another colour which may require a larger area. For example for fully saturated yellow to produce an harmonious balance with its complementary colour, violet, it should take up only one quarter of the area; fully saturated orange should only take up one third of the area of its complementary blue; fully saturated red and green should be present in equal proportions. If the saturation or tonal value of the hues is altered, the balancing areas of the complementaries will change.

If one colour is allowed to dominate, its colour characteristics will influence the expressive mood. Colours which are present in only a small amount seem to become relatively more vivid than if present in quantity (see pages 136–7).

Diagram (N) overleaf shows primary and secondary colours in harmonious proportion. Diagram (O) overleaf shows how a few small red squares appear highly active in a field of green.

Spatial relationships

If different colours are placed together certain colours may appear to advance forwards from the others, and another colour will appear to retreat. The effect is created by the colour relationships.

Sometimes the effect is desirable, for example to create the feeling of depth in a landscape painting. Sometimes it is undesirable, unbalancing a colour arrangement by making the colours jump about, forwards and backwards.

On a black background light tones appear to advance in front of it, whereas on a white background dark tones appear to advance. Warm tones tend to advance in front of cold ones; a pure colour tends to advance in front of a less pure one of equal tone (see diagram on page 15). If two colours of equal size are placed on the same colour background, one can appear larger than the other.

The diagrams in (P) on page 53 show how yellow retreats into a white background but advances from a black background. Red advances from a white background but retreats into a black one. The black background makes the yellow square look smaller and the red square bigger.

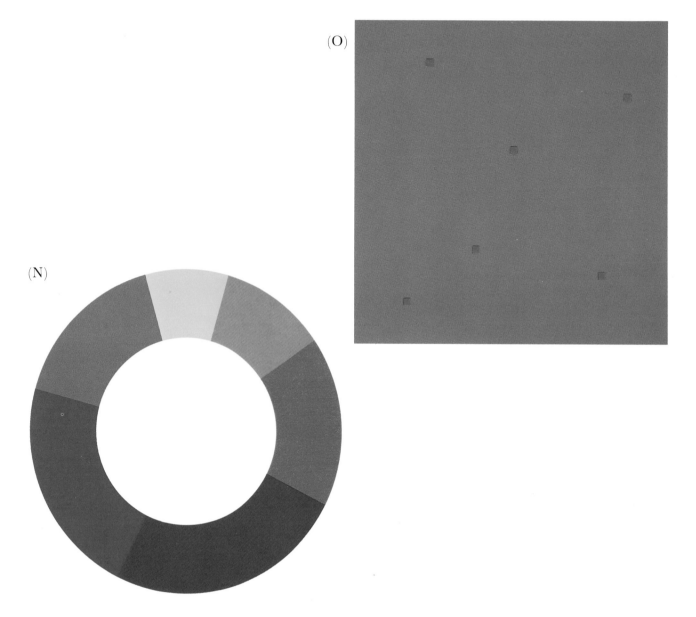

(O)

(N)

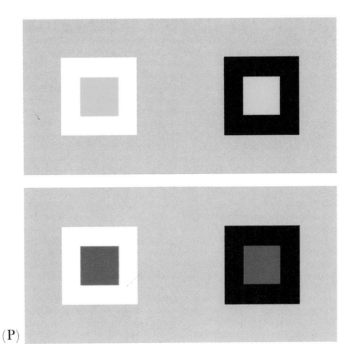

(P)

Coloured light

Coloured light can dramatically alter the appearance of a specific hue and the relationships between colours. The colour illustrations in this book are intended to be viewed by daylight, and it is an interesting experiment to look at them under different types of light to see how they change. The more intensely coloured the light source, the greater will be the alteration (see pages 104–5).

White light which is only lightly tinted with colour can have many uses in domestic settings. For example pink light is flattering and warming and peach coloured light is the most flattering to the complexion. Blue light can be relaxing, although it makes the complexion look grey.

PIGMENTS AND DYES

Modern scientists have the ability to produce paints and dyes in great variety and can create any colour that is asked for. It is said that over 3 million dyes and pigments have now been discovered, and that over 9,000 of these are marketed (see pages 116–17). Most modern pigments and dyes come from petroleum products. In practice, there are limitations on what can be made available commercially as some colours are very expensive to produce and some involve processes which are potentially dangerous to health or could pollute the atmosphere. Certain dyes and pigments are not durable and would not, therefore, be suitable for outside use or for cars and machinery.

The pigments and dyes that are available for everyday use depend on what the marketing departments decide to promote. For example, more white paint is sold than any other. A few years ago most of this was 'brilliant' white, and the market for it was very competitive. ICI then launched a range of new 'natural' white paints, which were, in effect, very pale shades of green, pink, and other colours. The paints caught the public's imagination, and enabled ICI to capture a larger share of this competitive market. But there was nothing technically or

RIGHT: *An artist's palette.*

chemically new about the paints (see pages 154–7).

Scientists first began to discover new dyes and pigments in a systematic and comprehensive way in the mid 19th century. Until then there were very few to choose from, and they were all produced from natural products – from the earth, plants, insects or animals, although the processes that turned them into suitable pigments and dyes could be quite complex. New industries with commercial laboratories and factories producing cheap synthetic materials grew up to meet the growing demand for these pigments and dyes, but as a result many old traditional industries declined and disappered. For example, the European madder fields which, for centuries, had produced the all-important red dye from the madder plant were wiped out. By 1914 the Indian indigo farms, which had produced a purple-blue dye for Western Europe, were completely devastated.

A pigment is a colouring substance which can be used as a paint or a dye. To make paint, the colouring substance is suspended in a medium. A medium is a suitable liquid which does not alter the colouring substance, and which dries with a hard surface. When a paint is

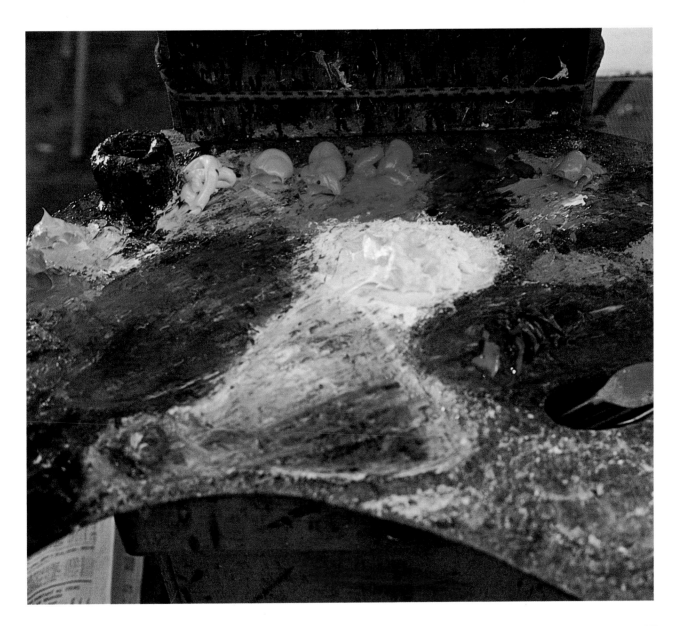

applied, the pigment coats the surface of the material, for example a cloth or a panel, and does not combine with it. The most commonly found mediums for painting pictures are egg yolk for egg tempera, various oils such as linseed or poppy for oil painting, water soluble gums for water colour, and modern synthetic resins for acrylics.

It was only in the 19th century that the commercial manufacture of artist's materials became so widespread that suitable paints could be easily bought in tubes over the counter at a shop. Before then the preparation of pigments and the making of paint had often involved long hours of grinding and preparing the materials, and had been an essential part of the artist's training and craft.

A dye is a colouring matter which works as a stain. Thus, when a cloth is dyed, the colouring matter reacts chemically with the fibres of the cloth, and colours them all the way through. For dyes to work, however, the fabric must contain a suitable substance so that this chemical reaction can take place. This is called a tanning substance, and fabrics frequently have to be treated with a mordant, which enables the dyes to be absorbed. In the past, mordants were found in river water, mud, fruit peels, rushes, mosses, ferns, fungi, and other natural substances, but it was a hit and miss affair to know or discover which mordant worked with which dye on which fabric. Different mordants could produce different colours from the same dye stuff. Understandably, once discovered, processes were guarded as precious secrets, and were kept in the same family or group and handed on from generation to generation.

Today all these processes can be analysed with accuracy in the laboratory. New man-made fibres have required the invention of new dyestuffs since they would not accept the old dyes. One of the major discoveries occurred in the 1950s when ICI discovered a new range of cheap, fast, bright dyestuffs called Procions that could be bonded to cellulose fibres. These had a great impact on the fashions of the 1960s (see pages 134–5).

The scientific analysis of pigments and paints is important in the restoration of paintings, and for establishing authenticity. Modern techniques enable pigments to be identified with great accuracy. The restorer needs to know what materials were originally used, especially when working on paintings of great rarity or value. Fakes, forgeries and copies can sometimes be revealed by showing that there are materials in the picture which would not have been available to the artist who is supposed to have painted it.

A Moroccan tannery.

Red pigments and dyes

The oldest known paintings are the famous cave murals at Lascaux in the Dordogne in the South of France (discovered in 1940), and those at Altamira near Santander in Northern Spain (discovered in 1879). Both were painted in the Stone Age, about 12,000 BC, and show a very high degree of artistic and technical competence. The main pigments used were red and yellow earths which obtain their colour from a high iron content, and which are quite common.

The coloured earths were ground into powder and kept in hollow bones which were plugged at one end. When needed for painting the powder was mixed with melted fat and applied to the walls with a simple brush made of animal hairs, with feather and twigs, or with the fingers. Sometimes powdered pigment was blown onto a prepared wall to produce a stencil effect. White and black are the two other pigments which were used, black being mainly the soot of the fire or charcoal, and white being chalk.

Iron oxide has been one of the most important sources of red pigment from the very earliest times, and is still commercially important today, although modern oxides are produced in the laboratory rather than dug out of the

Cadmium red dye being prepared by Winsor and Newton paints.

ground. Iron oxide in its natural state can have a wide variation in colour, ranging from dark purple to dull yellow. Some of the names reveal the source of the pigment, such as Venetian Red and Tuscan Red. One of the best sources of natural red oxide is Ormuz in the Persian Gulf.

The Egyptians had a wider and more sophisticated palette than the painters of the Stone Age and they used much better quality earth pigments which gave brighter colours. They introduced a new red pigment, called cinnabar, which was a heavy hard rock which was crushed and ground. It was also used by the Greeks and Romans. The best supplies of cinnabar came from Spain, probably from the Almadén mines which today are an important source of mercury.

The Greeks introduced two other red pigments, vermilion and red lead. Vermilion was the best bright red pigment known to the Classical World and the Middle Ages. It was an artificial form of cinnabar, formed by the combination of mercury and sulphur. The mixture produced a black powder which developed its red colour by grinding – the longer the grinding the finer the colour. Red lead was made by heating white lead, and it is still widely used today as an anti-corrosive pigment for iron. Both vermilion and red lead are, of course, poisonous.

Another early red pigment was red madder, also known as alizarin. It was a dye produced from the root of a plant *Rubia tinctorum* and was also used by the Egyptians. The madder plant is a native of Greece, and it was introduced into France and Italy at the time of the Crusades. Production of a dye from the madder plant called Turkey red was widely used in the textile industry, and its manufacture in natural form continued until the mid 19th century when two German chemists discovered how to make artificial alizarin. Alizarin was the first of the natural dyestuffs to be manufactured artificially, and so stands as an important landmark in the history of organic chemistry. The natural dye was notably used for French military cloth.

Another major discovery in the early 19th century was the metal cadmium. By mid century yellow cadmium pigments were produced, and in 1910 cadmium red was produced commercially for the first time. Cadmium red has largely replaced vermilion on the artist's palette as it is extremely durable. Also, there is a world shortage of vermilion.

Wool drying, Marrakesh.

Orange pigments and dyes

Until the end of the 19th century artists did not have a complete range of bright colour pigments which covered the full range of the spectrum. Red and blue were well represented with bright stable pigments. Yellow and green were adequately represented, but there was no natural organic or inorganic material which would produce a pure bright orange pigment. Orange could be produced by mixing red and yellow, but a colour produced by mixing is always less bright than the individual colours introduced (see pages 34–5).

Therefore an artist who wanted to introduce orange had to improvise. Some red and yellows incline towards orange, such as red lead and Indian yellow. Realgar is a variation of the yellow pigment orpiment, and is orange-red in colour. It was said to get its name from the Arabic Rahj al ghar (powder of the mine) and it was used mainly in Eastern miniatures and manuscripts and in Venetian paintings. Raw sienna is a special kind of yellow ochre, so called because it comes from the hill town of Siena in Tuscany, but the colour is brownish rather than orange. Burnt sienna is a warm reddish colour which was often mixed with the yellow pigment gamboge to create orange.

The major developments in the 19th century made bright orange available as a pigment for the first time. In 1770 an

ABOVE: *Orange pigment being blended into a binding agent for water colours.*

LEFT: *A wool souk, Marrakesh.*

orange coloured mineral was found in the Beresof gold mine in Siberia. It was eventually found to be a compound of lead with a new element which was called chromium because of the wide range of colours that could be obtained from it. Orange, green and yellow chromium pigments were in production in the early years of the 19th century.

The discovery of the metal cadmium and the subsequent development of the cadmium pigments in the mid 19th century enabled a deep orange to be made. Artificial ochres, known as Mars colours, were introduced at the end of the 18th century, including Mars orange. In the 1930s a new brilliant orange, called Molybdate orange, was introduced.

Yellow pigments and dyes

ABOVE: *Sulphur springs at Dallol in Ethiopia.*

RIGHT: *Yellow paint being ground in a 'roll mill'.*

The cave painters of Lascaux and Altamira used yellow ochre which is a natural earth whose colour can vary from pale yellow to reddish brown. It is found all over the world, and has, therefore, been used as a pigment by most civilisations. The best quality ochre comes from the Vaucluse in the south of France, but it is always a dull earthy yellow. The Egyptians introduced a brilliant, rich lemon yellow called orpiment, which is yellow sulphide of arsenic, and is highly poisonous. It is found in small quantities in the Near East, the Far East and Hungary, and must have been imported into Egypt where it is not found at all. It is referred to by the Classical writers Pliny and Vitruvius, and is mentioned by Cennino Cennini in his *Craftsman's Handbook*. One of its greatest uses was for manuscript illumination, and it has been identified on Byzantine, Persian, European and Irish manuscripts.

A variety of compounds of lead have been used as yellow pigments and given a confusing variety of names such as lead tin yellow, Naples yellow and massicot. They could range from a lemon colour to a deep yellow, but they were not intense colours and so they gradually fell out of favour.

Two organic pigments which have an unusual origin are gamboge and Indian yellow. Gamboge is a yellow gum resin obtained from several species of trees found in India, Ceylon, Siam and Cambodia. The name is a corruption of the word Cambodia. It is collected by cutting incisions in the trees from which run a yellowish brown milky juice which hardens in the air. It came to Europe quite early and was imported into England in the early 17th century by the East India Company. Indian Yellow was made in Bengal with the urine of cows that had been fed on mango leaves. The urine was heated to precipitate a yellow substance that was then pressed into lumps the size of cricket balls and dried. Its manufacture is now prohibited by law, but it produced a very beautiful colour.

One of the major developments at the beginning of the 19th century was the discovery and development of the chrome pigments. Chrome yellow was one of the most important of these, and seems to have been available early on in the 19th century; but supplies of the raw material were scarce, and it was after the discovery of deposits of chrome ore in the United States in 1820 that the pigment was manufactured in quantity. It is not an expensive pigment and it is still in use today. There are several versions of chrome yellow. Lemon yellow, a compound of barium and chromium, is a pale yellow; strontium chromate is deeper, and there is a compound of zinc and chromium.

Cadmium yellow was available commercially after about 1846 and was shown at the Great Exhibition of 1851. Cobalt yellow or aureolin was first introduced as an artist's pigment in 1861. Among the most permanent of modern synthetic yellow dyes is the range of Hansa yellows which were discovered by the Hoechst company in Germany.

Green pigments and dyes

Malachite, a natural green pigment.

The oldest of the green pigments is malachite. It was used by the ancient Egyptians and by the Chinese, and was widely used in European paintings until about 1800, when it was replaced by artificial green pigments. Malachite is a copper ore and is found in varying shades from apple green to emerald green. Mined in large chunks it is then prepared as a pigment by careful selection, grinding and sieving. It was much used for painting trees and foliage, and had the advantage that it did not deteriorate and go brown.

The Greeks introduced verdigris (the word is a corruption of *vert de Grece*) which is a greenish blue, but it is what is called a fugitive colour – ie the colour runs away or disappears with time – and eventually goes dark brown. There were various recipes for its preparation, and the Classical writer Pliny describes how it was made by exposing copper to the vapour of fermenting grape skins, or by putting copper plates and sour wine together in closed vats. Green matter collected on the copper plates, and this was finally scraped off and moulded into lumps. It was used for manuscript illumination, but sometimes the pigment has eaten into the parchment so that the painted parts have dropped out, leaving a hole in the page. There is not much green in early paintings, and it is important to remember that trees which may look brown now were green when originally painted.

Green earth (*terre verte*) was also used from early times. It is made from a marine clay which has a natural soft sage green colour. Suitable clay is found near

Verona, Italy, in Cornwall, England, and in Germany, France and Cyprus. Green earth was more suited to egg tempera than to oil painting. The pigment was used in Roman wall paintings. Renaissance painters used it as a foundation for flesh tones. They would apply a transparent flesh coloured glaze over the green earth, and the greenish reflection through the pink glaze gave a

Winsor and Newton water colour paints drying on heated slabs.

rich lustre to the flesh tones. Sometimes you will see damaged paintings in which the flesh coloured glaze has been removed. The green face that remains is not, of course, the one that the artist intended you to see (see page 76).

An artificial pigment called emerald green was first made in 1814. It is a bright blue-green, but it was not widely used, one reason being that it is a compound of arsenic and, therefore, highly toxic. Indeed, it has been sold commercially as an excellent rat poison and insecticide! It was sometimes used in the early 19th century as a wallpaper colouring, and it is now believed to have been responsible for the death of Napoleon. As a prisoner on St Helena his green wallpaper decomposed releasing a toxic arsenic vapour which eventually poisoned him.

Alongside the chrome yellows that were introduced in the early 19th century, a chromium containing green known as viridian was produced. It is a bright green with none of the disadvantages of verdigris and emerald green, and it soon replaced them. In France it is called *vert émeraude*, which is confusing, because it is not poisonous emerald green. Also, the so-called chrome green is, in fact, a mixture of Prussian blue and chrome yellow. Cobalt green, which is a bluish green, was introduced in 1835, and monastral green in the 1930s.

Blue pigments and dyes

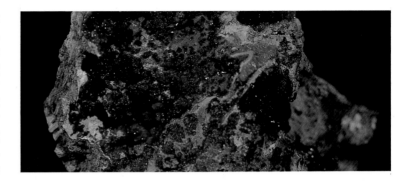

A piece of azurite from Eire, Ireland.

Azurite was one of the earliest and most important blue pigments. It was a natural pigment derived from a basic copper carbonate. Prepared by washing and grinding, it occurs naturally all over the world. It was used in ancient Egypt and in the Near East, and was widely used in the wall paintings of the Sung and Ming Dynasties of China. It is often found in European paintings from the 15th century to the 17th century. The principal source of azurite at this time was Hungary, and it ceased to be readily available after Hungary was overrun by the Turks in the mid 1600s.

The Egyptians introduced another blue pigment which was known as Alexandra blue, or Egyptian blue frit. They had a well-developed technique for manufacturing opaque coloured glass, and finely ground blue glass gave them this pigment.

Blue glass was the basis for another pigment used in European paintings from the late 16th to the early 19th centuries. Known as smalt, it was the earliest of the cobalt pigments (see page 80). Cobalt was used in medieval stained glass and by the Venetian glass makers. Important cobalt mines were found in Germany (Bohemian glass is noted for its fine blue colour) and, later, the best smalt was prepared in Holland. Smalt had several drawbacks, the most fundamental being its transparency. It was eventually superseded by the synthetic pigments which were produced in the 19th century, notably cobalt blue which was discovered in 1802. Cerulean blue, which was introduced in 1860, is a type of cobalt blue, and is the only cobalt blue pigment without a violet tint.

The most notable contribution to the history of pigments by the Italian Renaissance was the introduction of ultramarine. They discovered a method of extracting a brilliant blue pigment from the semi-precious stone lapis lazuli. The best quality material came from the East, notably Afghanistan. The word ultramarine means 'from overseas'. Cennino Cennini describes at length how the stone was ground, mixed into a waxy paste, and then kneaded and washed to release the pigment. Ultramarine was a very expensive pigment, but very fine in colour and very stable. A cheap alternative was Blue Verditer, but this gave a pale greenish blue pigment, which in time tended to become green. The chemical composition of ultramarine was identified in 1806, and shortly afterwards the French government offered a prize for the manufacture of an inexpensive artificial ultramarine. It was won by a M. Guimet from Toulouse. Artificial ultramarine, which is widely used as an artist's pigment, is often called 'French Ultramarine' presumably because of its French origin.

The first artificially prepared modern colour was Prussian Blue. This was discovered, by accident, by a German between 1704 and 1710. He was trying to make red pigment, and added potash contaminated with animal oil. The end result was a very strong dark blue. It was widely used as it was much cheaper than ultramarine.

Indigo is a blue dye which was originally obtained from plants, the best quality being found in India and China. It was used as a dye by the Egyptians and the Romans, and was imported into Europe from the 17th century onwards with the expansion of the trade routes. Woad is a blue dye very similar to indigo. A process for making synthetic indigo was discovered in 1880 (see page 133).

Monastral blue, which is very close to the ideal pure blue in that it reflects only green and blue light, was developed by ICI in 1935. It was very important for the development of high quality three colour printing, which requires as pure a blue as possible (see pages 40–41). Manganese blue was discovered in 1935. It is green-blue in colour, and because it is very stable and inert chemically it is widely used for colouring cement.

Cotton being dyed with indigo, Indonesia.

Violet pigments and dyes

Natural violet and purple pigments are very few. The Romans used a purple dye which was made from a shellfish similar to a whelk. It was called Tyrian purple as the best quality was made at Tyre on the east coast of the Mediterranean. It was extremely costly, but it was also highly important, and was used for the togas of Roman Emperors. The shellfish is found on the shores of the Mediterranean and Atlantic coast, including the British Isles, and heaps of the shells are still found at the sites of the ancient

Murex brandaris –
the shellfish used by the
Romans to make
purple dye.

dye works. The shellfish produces a secretion which is contained in a little vein, and when this is broken it yields a white fluid. Cloths to be dyed are dipped in this fluid, and when they are exposed to strong sunlight it changes to a purplish red or crimson. Each shellfish yields only a tiny amount of fluid – hence the very high cost – but the dye is very stable and long lasting.

Cochineal (sometimes called carmine lake or crimson lake) is another natural organic dye. It is made from the dried bodies of the female insect coccus cacti which lives on cactus plants in Mexico and Central America. There are chemical processes in which the cochineal extract is turned into pigments, and the colour can vary between red and deep purple. Cochineal was brought to Europe shortly after the conquest of Mexico in 1523. Unlike Tyrian purple the colours fade in strong sunlight.

Until the mid 19th century there was no satisfactory and stable purple pigment for painters to use. Purple and violet are found in old master paintings, but they are always created indirectly rather than with a purple or violet pigment. Old master painters used glazes, which are thin layers of transparent paint which can be laid like varnish on top of areas

Cobalt violet being ground for Winsor and Newton.

of dry paint. The different colours of the glazes gave subtle changes and nuances of colour, and one of the many ways of creating the effect of purple was to glaze with red lake over a layer of vermilion, blue and white lead.

In 1856 there was a major chemical discovery. Sir William Perkin made the first synthetic dyestuff through a distillation of coal tar products. These were called aniline dyes and they revolutionised the dyeing industry. Mauve, which is reddish violet, was the first of the aniline dyes. Magenta, a red-purple, is another dye which was first prepared in the mid 19th century (see page 156).

Black pigments and dyes

The earliest black pigment was soot. The painters of the caves at Lascaux and Altamira would have taken a charred stick from their fire and used it to make a black mark on the surface of the wall. Fire and smoke has always been an important source of black pigment. Pliny describes the production of Lamp Black by the Romans. Oil, tar, pitch or resin was burned in brick chambers, and the smoke produced carbon which was collected to produce a black pigment that had a bluish tinge. A more modern method of production is to play the smoky flame from natural gas on to a cooled revolving metal drum with scrapers to remove the black deposit. This is known as carbon black, and it is brownish black in colour. Ivory black is made by charring the waste cuttings of ivory, and then grinding them to a black residue. It is the most intense of the black pigments. Animal bones can also be used, but it produces a black which is less intense and has a bluish tinge.

Sepia is the black or dark brown secretion of the squid. It is very strong – the secretion from one squid can turn a thousand gallons of water opaque in a few seconds. To make the pigment the ink sacs are removed from the fish, dried, pulverised and boiled. Sepia soon turns reddish brown or yellow brown, and this is the colour most commonly associated with the name.

Asphaltum or bitumen was a pigment much used in England in the 18th century. As its name suggests, it is an oily, tarry substance, and it was imported from the Caucasus or the borders of the Dead Sea. Being an oily substance it never dries properly, and is very unstable. In warm weather it literally moves on the surface of a painting, so destroying that area of the picture. Sir Joshua Reynolds used it regularly for the backgrounds of his portraits because, initially, it gave a succulent browny black. Unfortunately all that can be seen now is a dead looking, cracked area, quite unlike the effect he wanted.

Sepia is obtained from the ink sacs of the squid.

A painting of Anne Stanley, later Lady Mendip, by Sir Joshua Reynolds (detail).

White pigments and dyes

The most important pigment in the history of Western painting is white lead. It is virtually the only white pigment used in easel paintings from the earliest times until the 19th century.

The Greeks made white lead by the 'stack process', which was refined by the Dutch in the 17th century to produce the best white lead ever made. In the process, strips of metallic lead are placed in clay pots which have separate compartments at the bottom into which is poured a weak solution of vinegar. The pots are placed in a shed with manure or tanner's bark and the building is closed. The resulting interaction of heat, carbon dioxide from the bark, vapour from the vinegar, oxygen and water vapour turns the lead to basic lead carbonate. This is then washed and dried and ground with linseed oil to produce the all important painting material.

A side benefit of the use of white lead is that it enables us to look under the surface of a painting with the use of X-rays. Some artists make many changes as they work, and they cover their changes with layers of paint until they reach the final result. Lead absorbs X-rays, and the greater the amount of lead the greater the absorption of X-rays.

Because white lead is so widely used, and mixed with other pigments, an X-ray of a painting reveals the underlying marks and brushstrokes made by the artist which cannot be seen by the naked eye.

Zinc white and titanium white are now used more often than white lead, but neither allows X-ray analysis to be carried out as effectively. Zinc white does not go black on exposure to air and is not poisonous like white lead but it lacks opacity or hiding power, and it was not until the mid 19th century that Winsor and Newton invented a process for making it less transparent. They marketed their new pigment under the name 'Chinese White'. Zinc white is colder and purer than white lead.

Titanium white is the purest white and has the best covering and hiding power of any of the white pigments. It is also very stable and is unaffected by heat, light or air. Titanium ore had been known about since the end of the 18th century, but it was not until the 1920s that an economic method of manufacture was worked out. It is now the largest selling white pigment, and the development of titanium white has been the major modern contribution to the history of pigments and dyes.

This X-ray shot of Tarquin and Lucretia *by* Titian *shows the underpainting and alterations made by the artist, notably the change in position of the man's right arm. See page 78 for the complete painting.*

COLOUR IN PAINTINGS

From the cave paintings at Lascaux to the latest experiments in Contemporary Art, artists have used all the colour materials that have been available to them. The twenty paintings that are illustrated in this part of the book have been chosen because they each show one or more of the ways in which artists can use or have used colour. In some cases it is the pigment which is more important, for example the cloak of the Virgin Mary in a religious altarpiece that has been painted with the best quality materials as a mark of respect for her status (see page 76) or a modern painter who has used the then newly introduced acrylic paints which flow as easily as water but have bright colours and can stain like a dye (see page 94). In some cases colour has been used to express an idea or emotion, for example Titian using bright red to convey lust and passion, or van Gogh using red and green to convey anguish and despair. Sometimes colour has been used to create an illusion – the way the deep and open space of a land-scape can be made to appear three-dimensional on the flat surface of a picture is a good example. Sometimes colour has been used to recreate the sensation of natural light. In some of the paintings the artist has combined several uses of colour together in one picture, and in nearly all cases colour has also been used for the joy of colour itself.

The history of pigments and dyes shows that until relatively recently artists were restricted in the colours that were available to them. Renaissance artists made a great leap forward in developing a new realistic style in painting, and it is often forgotten that they also made significant developments in painting techniques to make the most of their limited colour range. They perfected the techniques of painting with egg tempera, and fresco painting on walls of wet white plaster. They introduced oil painting techniques, and with new and better pre-pared materials, oil paints enabled them to create richer and more subtle colours (see pages 76–80).

The next major development in colour came in the 19th century. The newly introduced colourful paints and pig-ments (see page 56) were taken up with enthusiasm by the Romantics such as Turner at the beginning of the century, and by the Impressionists such as Monet at the end of it. But all these develop-ments and experiments with colour are overshadowed by what has happened in the 20th century. The range of colour and materials that artists can now use is

almost overwhelming. Artists have used colour to push forward the old boundaries which restricted perception, ideas, and emotions. The great masters of Modern Art such as Matisse and Picasso used new colours to develop new forms of art, and a free attitude towards their use helped to create abstract painting.

Children use colour instinctively and vividly. Many modern artists attempt to capture this direct spontaniety.

Until the late 19th century, skill with colour always took second place to skill with drawing. Now the position is reversed, but even the most knowledgeable painters are still learning what colour can do. The art of drawing took many centuries to develop. The art of colour still has a very long way to go.

Duccio di Buoninsegna (active 1278–1319) *The Virgin and Child with Saints* **National Gallery, London**

This altarpiece with hinged doors was painted as a commission. There would have been a contract specifying in detail what the artist was to do, and the materials that he was to use. The Virgin's robe has been painted with the best quality ultramarine. Blue is the appropriate colour for the Virgin (see page 24) and it was considered that she should be painted with only the most costly materials (see pages 66–7). The face looks green because the green earth that was used as an under-paint has become more

prominent with the passing of time. The layers of flesh coloured paint which covered the green have either worn away or become more transparent (see page 64).

The altarpiece is painted in egg tempera, ie the pigments have been mixed with egg yolk. This produces a very strong and permanent layer of paint, but because it dries quickly it has to be applied in small brushstrokes. It is not possible to apply egg tempera thickly or to work it into other areas of wet paint, as can be done with oil paints. (Oil paints were not introduced until the 15th century.) (See page 54.)

Early altarpieces were painted in bright saturated colours which were able to hold their own against the shining gold backgrounds. Bright colours were also necessary in altarpieces which were used in churches where they had to compete with brightly coloured interior decoration, and were often only seen by candlelight.

Michelangelo (1475–1564) *Eleazar and Mathan* **Fresco from the upper wall of the Sistine Chapel, Rome**

Michelangelo's paintings on the ceiling of the Sistine Chapel in Rome have recently been cleaned, and the fresh bright colours which he originally chose can now be seen. Over the years, the Sistine Chapel ceiling had become covered in smoke and grime from the

candlelight and atmosphere, depositing a dark film over the frescos. Some experts argued that Michelangelo himself had put a dark varnish over his paintings to dull the colours, but the cleaning has proved that this was not so, and revealed that he used colour as brightly and intensely as he could.

Michelangelo used the technique of fresco, in which white plaster is used as the medium to hold the pigments. The pigments are dissolved in water, and applied to plaster that is still wet. The colour is drawn into the plaster which then dries out, leaving a very permanent result. The painting and the colours should last unchanged as long as the plaster. The white plaster acts as the white pigment, which is why frescos always have a 'chalky' look.

Fresco is a difficult technique because the artist has to work very quickly, applying a thin layer of wet plaster to a small area of wall or ceiling. He has to work directly onto it before it dries and has no time to include complicated details, nor can he correct any mistakes. As the plaster dries the colours tend to become lighter, and they cannot be readjusted. For these reasons fresco painters used bold and direct designs with large areas of colour.

Titian (c 1487–1576) *Tarquin and Lucretia* Fitzwilliam Museum, Cambridge

The picture shows a dramatic moment in one of the famous stories of early Roman history. A virtuous noble woman, Lucretia, was raped by Sextus, the son of a tyrant. He attacked her in her room, and threatened that unless she yielded, he would kill her and her servant, and make it appear that they had committed adultery together. Lucretia gave in to the threat, but she then wrote to her father and husband to tell them what had happened, and stabbed herself to death.

Titian's exciting composition catches all the drama of the story, and he uses colour to heighten the impact. The bright red stockings and breeches worn by Sextus suggest the blood, the lust, and the wrongdoing which are central to the story. This hot red also contrasts with the pure cool white of the linen sheets and pillows, and emphasises the warm pure flesh tones of Lucretia's naked body.

Titian has worked with oil paints. This has allowed him to alter and adjust the painting as he worked at it, and to produce exceptionally rich glowing colours. The range of colours is, in fact, quite limited but Titian uses contrasts of light and dark, hot and cold, and strong accents of white and red to make colour work to give the appropriate emotional and visual impact.

El Greco (1541–1614) *Expulsion of the Traders from the Temple* **National Gallery, London**

This picture shows a well-known scene from the New Testament. The setting is the Temple in Jerusalem. Christ is in the centre, brandishing a whip. Around him are the money changers and the traders in sheep, cattle and pigeons who sold their animals and birds for sacrifice. In an angry outburst he drives them out of the temple, and they flee in general confusion.

El Greco painted this picture for people who would have known the story well, but he offered them a new interpretation. Although the scene is one of chaos and confusion he uses large areas of bright colour to create an orderly pattern and so hold the composition of the picture together. Also, he has used colour in a symbolic way to bring out the meaning of the story and make it more dramatic. The inside of the temple is dark, and it is painted in a muddy brown. The flesh and limbs of the traders are also painted in the same unattractive colour. Outside the temple, through the archway, there are buildings which are in the sunlight, glowing white under a blue sky.

The archway surrounds the head of Christ, rather like a halo. The clarity of the light and the whiteness of the buildings symbolise purity, contrasting with the darkness inside. Only the clothes of the people are painted in bright colours. Those of the traders are mainly golden yellow, symbolising their love of money. El Greco has contrasted the golden yellow with patches of cool blue and green to increase the visual impact. Christ is dressed in red, to symbolise his anger, but his robe catches the light so that he shines like a beacon in the dark interior.

Rembrandt (1606–1669) *The Adoration of the Shepherds* **1646 National Gallery, London**

Rembrandt used a very limited range of colours, which were mainly earth colours and black. For red he used vermilion, and for blue, azurite and smalt (see page 66). His green was probably made by mixing these blues with lead tin yellow (see page 62). Although the range of colours in this picture is small, the light-dark contrasts create a wonderful impression of glowing light (see page 50). Indeed, had he utilised a wider range of bright colours he might have destroyed this particular effect.

The warm browns, yellows and reds are lightened with white to create the focus of light around the cradle, so that it appears to be the source of the light. The same reds and browns are darkened to create the shadows and half lights, some of which have a green or blue tinge and therefore appear cooler. The brightly lit area, which is the focus of the picture, and which is an area of light colour on a dark background, also seems to stand forward out of the dark shadows.

Rembrandt would have learned how to use colour and light-dark contrasts when he was a pupil, and also learned by careful observation and experiment. He painted straight onto his canvases, without making drawings first, so he would have adjusted his colours and con-

trasts as he worked. He used oil paints, which dry slowly, so allowing him to blend light and dark areas together without hard outlines.

Claude Lorraine (1600–1682) *Landscape with David at the Cave of Abdullam* National Gallery, London

Claude was one of the early masters of pure landscape painting. This is a typical work in which he shows an ideal world, a serene countryside lit by delicate sunlight which stretches gently to the far horizon. He uses colour in two ways to create this dreamlike image. The harmonious mood is reflected in the harmony of soft colours. He also uses a technique called 'aerial perspective' to create the illusion of deep space. He uses warm reddish colours in the foreground which give the appearance of advancing forwards relative to the green tones in the middle distance. Similarly the blue tones in the far distance appear to recede. We now know that there is an explanation for this general phenomenon in which reds appear to advance and blues retreat (see pages 37 and 51). In the 17th century this knowledge and understanding was not available, and this is another example of the way artists learned by experiment and experience how to use colour.

John Constable (1776–1837) *Flatford Mill* **1817 Tate Gallery, London**

One of Constable's aims was to capture in his paintings the sensation of 'dewy freshness' which can be seen, felt and smelt in nature. He chose his subjects carefully so that they would express his love of natural beauty and the cultivation of the earth. He started with small sketches done out of doors, and from there he developed his major pictures.

Constable used colour to build up his desire for dewy freshness in a variety of ways. In this early work he has been careful to record the precise greens that he has observed in nature, and he has used them throughout the picture. He has made them come alive by using a wide variety of different greens and weaving them together so that the eye is gently stimulated as it moves across them. He also includes small accents of red, the complementary of green, through flowers in the grass and the jacket of the boy. If these accents were taken away the impression of sparkling green would be very much diminished. Constable did not know of the theory of complementary colours, so he is using the contrast of red and green instinctively rather than theoretically (see page 47).

Constable has not used the formula for aerial perspective, ie a warm red in the foreground and a cool blue in the distance (see page 81). He disapproved of such techniques considering them to be artificial and not true to life.

J. M. W. Turner (1775–1851) *Norham Castle, Sunrise* Tate Gallery, London

Turner first went to Italy when he was 44, and already a successful artist. Italian light, with its warm golden glow, made an enormous impact on him, and he gradually turned away from the rather dark and traditional colours of his early pictures to a palette that used luminous yellow, reds and blues. Turner was very interested in the emotional impact of colours, and he tried to put into practice some of the ideas which had been developed by his contemporary, the German poet and philosopher, Johann Goethe, who wrote a treatise on colour. In the early 19th century new pigments were becoming available to artists, especially the chrome colours, and these helped Turner to develop and brighten his palette (see page 63).

Norham Castle is on the English Scottish border, but in this late work Turner has used the bright luminous colours that he first saw in Italy. It is an unfinished picture, and may have been painted by Turner as an experiment. He enhances the sensation of delicate glowing light by painting the castle as a soft cool blue in a surrounding area of a pale cool yellow. These are contrasting colours which vibrate together, but he has ensured that the contrast is not too strong (see page 48). He has then enhanced the coolness of the early morning light by adding a small contrasting accent of warm red by means of the cow in the foreground.

Eugène Delacroix (1798–1863)
***Women of Algiers* 1834 Louvre, Paris**

This picture was painted after Delacroix had visited Morocco in 1832. He was excited by the bright light of North Africa, for it enabled him to study colour, reflections and shadows. He noted how shadows were tinged with the complementary colour of the area in bright light – for example how a man with a reddish complexion has greenish shadows on his face. The sketches that he made for this painting show that he had noted how the red skirt had violet shadows, and he also noted that if colours are toned down with grey they tend to go muddy, whereas if they are toned down by mixing them with their complementary colour they retain their clarity (see page 48). Delacroix's work is a subtle combination of the colour harmonies which he saw in old master paintings, and the colour relationships which he found by careful observation in nature. He was a great admirer of the Venetian School of painting (Titian, for example), and of Rubens and Velásquez. Like them he loved rich colour, and he was fortunate that during his lifetime many new pigments were becoming available to artists. Delacroix was respected by the painters of the late 19th century such as Manet, Degas, Cézanne and van Gogh. They appreciated the way in which he carefully observed and studied colour. He is the key figure who links the colour ideas of the old masters with the colour ideas of modern painters.

James Abbott McNeill Whistler (1834–1903) ***Miss Cicely Alexander: Harmony in Grey and Green* (detail) 1872 National Gallery, London**

Whistler often gave his pictures a double title, referring to the subject and also the colour arrangement. He was a leading figure in the Aesthetic Movement (Oscar Wilde was a friend). They believed that art and beauty were central to life, and that exquisite and harmonious arrangements of all kinds were very important. Whistler always painted with subdued and subtle colours which are finely balanced, and his paints were thin and transparent. He did not like bright colour compositions or strong contrasts of light and shade, which he considered vulgar. In this painting he has used a harmonious arrangement of greys and blacks, with areas of soft grey-green in the girl's sash, the feather in her hat and the bows on her shoes. Her pink face and arm and deep red lips are areas of warm colour which contrast with the cool greys, and the butterflies are an accent of soft brownish yellow which enlivens the flat pattern of grey (see page 49). Whistler liked to give the impression that his work was created effortlessly. He wanted people to think that his colour arrangements were the result of brilliant inspiration, and produced with no trouble. The truth was rather different. This portrait required over 70 sittings before he was satisfied with the result. Even for Whistler colour arrangements required a lot of thought and work, and much trial and error.

Claude Monet (1840–1926) *Autumn at Argenteuil* **1873 Courtauld Institute Galleries, London**

The Impressionist painters of the late 19th century were the first to employ a full range of the colours of the spectrum. One of their aims was to capture in paint the natural qualities of light, and they found that this was achieved more successfully with a palette of rainbow colours. Whereas old master painters had used white for highlights and black for shadows, the Impressionists adopted a new convention and technique. They used violet and blue for the shadows, and yellow and orange for the brightest daylight. The reason? On the colour wheel, which they had studied and understood, violet and yellow and blue and orange are complementaries, and when placed side by side they are perceived to vibrate together (see pages 12–13). This is an early work by Monet. He has recorded the colours of autumn with great accuracy, and at the same time has placed these vibrating colours together to recreate the quality of autumn light.

Georges Seurat (1859–1891) *Le Pont de Courbevoie* 1886–7 Courtauld Institute Galleries, London

Seurat has painted his picture with small dots of pure colour. This is the well-known *pointilliste* or divisionist technique which he developed with a small group of fellow artists.

Seurat studied the most up-to-date ideas on colour theory, and at the end of the 19th century there was much interesting and new research into the way we see colour and the way in which coloured light and colour pigments work. Seurat developed a system of painting based on his understanding of these new ideas. Instead of creating colour effects by mixing pigments, he applied unmixed dots of pure colour. His theory was that when his pictures were viewed from a distance the individual dots would not be seen, but that their colours would mix in the eye. In other words he was trying to create the effect of mixing light, for he believed that mixing pigments (subtractive colour mixing) could not achieve the same subtle and luminous qualities as

mixing light (see pages 34–5). He worked out his ideas in great detail, based on theory and close observation of light and shadow, and he explained at length how and where the coloured dots should be placed. In practice the theory turned out to be less than perfect, although it should be said that his experiments helped to advance our understanding of colour perception, and that he painted pictures which have their own remarkable and beautiful qualities of colour and light.

Vincent van Gogh (1853–1890) *The Night Café* **1888 Yale University Art Gallery, New Haven, USA**

Van Gogh used bright colours to express his turbulent emotions. He painted very quickly, often completing one picture a day, and he used the oil paint straight from the tube. He had an instinctive eye for colour and his emotional response was direct and rapid. This painting shows the café at Arles in the South of France where he spent many hours. He hoped to find peace and fulfilment at Arles, but in the end he found only anguish and disappointment, and shortly after he painted this picture he tried to commit suicide. Some of van Gogh's works shine with bright cheerful colours, and he uses yellow to express his optimism and love of light and nature. Here the mood is different, and he has darkened the yellow and used dull red and greens, with an accent of acid green, to express his depression. In a letter to his brother Theo he said of this picture: 'Everywhere there is a clash and contrast of the most alien reds and greens.... I have tried to express the terrible passions of humanity by means of red and green.'

Henri Matisse (1869–1954) *Landscape at Collioure* 1906 The State Hermitage Museum, Leningrad

Matisse was known as the 'King of Colour'. He said that working with colour was like a composer working with the notes of a musical scale. He was the leader of an avant-garde group of painters called the 'Fauves' – the wild beasts – who painted in bright colours and did not think it necessary to follow the colours in nature. They felt free to paint the sky yellow or a face green if the expression in their painting required it. The *Landscape at Collioure* is an early work painted in the South of France where Matisse was thrilled by the brightness of the light and the intensity of the colours. In this painting he is trying to recreate the atmosphere of warmth and the brilliant light and colour and so express his principal feeling and sensation. He uses bold areas

of colour but allows the white canvas to show through. These areas of white are important as they provide resting points for the eye, and allow the strong colours to 'breathe' and reach their full strength. He uses the full spectrum from red to violet, and deliberately uses harmonics and contrasts of colour. Notice how he uses green, for example. In the red foreground he places small accents of green as a contrasting complementary to accentuate the red, whereas in the background green is used to harmonise with the blue of the sea and the distant hill (see page 47).

Robert Delaunay (1885–1941) *Hommage à Blériot* 1914 Musée d'Art Moderne de la Ville de Paris

This picture tries to bring several ideas together, and colour is used as the link between them. In the background is the Eiffel Tower in Paris, and the aeroplane is the one in which Blériot first crossed the English Channel from France in 1909. Like many painters, writers and poets of the day, Delaunay was fascinated by modern communications, especially the recent inventions of radio and flight which seemed to have the ability to cut through space and time in a way that had not been done before. The Eiffel Tower had one of the first radio masts at the top of it. Delaunay was also fascinated by the way in which light can be broken up into pure prismatic colours (see pages 10–11), and by bright objects that have a glowing halo which seems to cut through and fill the space around them. He was one of the first painters to create purely abstract pictures, and in his early abstract works he used discs of bright colour to explore the relationship between light and space. In this work he has combined his interests in time and space and technology together. He uses a modern style of painting with an up-to-date perception of colour to celebrate Blériot's pioneering achievement, and to express his delight in the modern world.

Wassily Kandinsky (1866–1944) *In Blue* **1925 Nordrhein-Westfalen Museum, Düsseldorf**

Kandinsky was one of the pioneers of abstract painting in the first decades of the 20th century. He was unusually sensitive to colour and was deeply moved by its effects. He also had strongly developed powers of synaesthesia, which means that he experienced colour sensations when other senses, such as taste and hearing, were stimulated (see page 32).

One of the problems for the early abstract painters was this: if they ceased to create a recognisable subject matter, but painted pictures that were composed only of forms and colour, would they be able to create works of art which had a serious and spiritual or intellectual content, or would their works merely be decorative objects? Artists such as Kandinsky gradually established that abstract art could be more than decoration, and could aspire to the greatest heights.

In the 1920s Kandinsky was a Professor at the Bauhaus, alongside Itten and Klee, and in 1926 he wrote his treatise 'Point and Line to Plane' which discussed the relationships between colour and forms. To understand and appreciate Kandinsky's work you need to allow the colours and forms to act on their own, without trying to connect them with colours and shapes in daily life. It may help to think of it as the difference between walking around a familiar place, and trying to imagine what it must be like to be an astronaut taking a walk in space where there are no walls, no boundaries, no balance, and no reassuring pull of gravity. Like the astronaut you may find it possible to share a new, exhilarating, and 'unworldly' experience.

Karel Appel (born 1921) *Two Heads*
1958
Karel Appel has used very thick oil paint
and bright colours which have sometimes
been squeezed straight from the tube in
snaking lines. In other places he has
spread the oil paint and flattened it with
a knife. He has used strong clashing
colours and a rough technique to express
a sense of explosive energy. However, the
energy is not completely wild or uncon-
trolled. For example, there is a broad
curving form or shape which moves
across the picture from top to bottom,

and the more you look at the colours
the more they seem to fit together and
support each other. He has used the three
primary colours, red, yellow and blue,
and also added black and white. As was
noted on page 47, the three primary
colours together give the most intense
contrast of hue, and this contrast can be
strengthened by black and white.
Perhaps it is best to compare this painter
with a jazz musician or modern dancer.
Like them he is well trained. Just as they
know how to get the best out of their
musical instrument or body, and how far
they can push them, he understands how
oil paints and colour work, and how far
he can stretch them without disaster. It
is only when they have that knowledge
and confidence that a jazz musician or
dancer, or a painter like Karel Appel,
can let themselves go, and have the
freedom to improvise a composition
which can convey excitement and energy
in a way that other people can share.

Mark Rothko (1903–1970) *Painting 118* **1961 Museum of Fine Arts, Houston, Texas**

Rothko painted large scale abstract pictures which are characterised by simple shapes and soft outlines. To 'see' them properly you need to stand or sit close to them for a fairly long period of time, so that you become unaware of the edges of the painting, and find yourself lost in the sensation of colour. In this way colour will begin to have an emotional effect. For many people a painting by Rothko can be as moving as Beethoven's music, working in a very similar emotional manner. Some of his paintings use colours which are vibrant and joyful; others, particularly his later works, use sombre colours reflecting his own depression which led to his suicide.

Rothko's works have the ability to reflect his own emotions, which are those that we may all share at one time or another. He once said that he used colour 'to express ... basic human emotions – tragedy, ecstasy, doom ... The people who weep before my pictures are having the same religious experience I had when I painted them. And if you ... are moved only by their colour relationships, then you miss the point.'

Morris Louis (1912–1962) *Alpha-Phi* **1961 Tate Gallery, London**

Morris Louis was one of a small group of American artists who pioneered new techniques. His canvases were not painted in a conventional way by using pigments and brushes. He used very liquid acrylic paints which were poured onto the canvas so that they acted like a stain or dye, and soaked into the material (see page 54). He has controlled the flow of the paint and caused it to run in channels by moving the canvas. As he worked on a large scale this was a complicated procedure, and he sometimes needed scaffolding to support the canvas. One of the reasons for staining the canvas was that it enabled him to eliminate the texture which all paints have, and the marks which brushstrokes leave behind. In other words it enabled him to use colour in a very direct way, and to preserve the liquid free-flowing quality of fresh paint. The drawback to the technique is that no alterations or changes of mind could be made, and mistakes could not be corrected. As a result he destroyed many of the works which he had started.

In this painting streams of bright paint have been poured down each side of the canvas, and the large expanse of white canvas allows the eye to create flickering after images as it crosses from one side to the other (see page 49).

Bridget Riley (born 1931) *Cartoon for RA* Mayor Rowan Gallery, London

In 1981 Bridget Riley went to Egypt where she became fascinated by the colours that the ancient Egyptians had used (see page 22). They had retained the same range of colours – red, yellow, blue, turquoise and green, with black and white – for more than 3,000 years, and used them for all their decoration, including paintings, buildings, jewellery, furniture and pottery. The colours combined to produce very strong and exciting sensations which she had not seen before.

Bridget Riley is an artist with exceptional sensitivity to colour. She is intrigued by the way that colours can generate light, mood and activity, and the way in which individual colours have a life and identity of their own. She has used the stripe because this shape allows her to put colours together edge to edge over a long distance. When colours meet in this way they react against each other producing impressions and sensations in the eye and mind. They can alter their apparent colour, move in space, or cause the eye to see things that are not there at all (see pages 46–53). Her paintings need to be seen in real life, because it is only then that the actual hue and the size of the paintings work to produce these finely calculated effects.

COLOUR AND BUILDINGS:
Temples

The tradition of painting our houses goes back to the beginning of building and beyond – into the painted caves of our prehistoric ancestors. According to archaeologists, many of the earliest forms of architecture, such as the ziggurats of Mesopotamia and the Aztec pyramids, were either plated in metal and ceramic or covered in painted frescos. Also, the temples, palaces and sculpture of ancient Egypt and Greece were, in their original state, coloured in bright paintwork. This tradition also extended to the medieval cathedrals in Europe where the painted colour decoration was often more vivid on the outside than on the inside.

Even the Parthenon in Athens on its opening day in 432 BC was completely painted, red, blue, pink and gilding being applied to its friezes above lime-washed columns. It would be fascinating to know what motive drove its designer Phidias who, working without a modern Dulux or Crown Paint technology, completely decorated the inside and outside of his marble temple. The fact that he had to use inferior pigments as well as a limited colour range did not seem to deter him.

It is believed that the ancient painters and decorators used colour as a symbolic language. For example, the stages of the Mesopotamian ziggurats were colour-layered with the symbolic hues of the planets, the Mesopotamians being an astrologically motivated society. The Egyptian Temple of Karnak – considered by historians to be the most beautiful building ever erected – used green as part of its colour scheme to symbolise the fertility of the Nile (see page 22). The Sphinx had a red painted face because extremes of skin complexion were highly prized in ancient Egypt. The Greek word 'parthenon' implies virginity and purity. Possibly, for this reason Phidias painted his temple white, reserving bright hues for its friezes so that they could be clearly seen from below.

Although much of the ancient's use of colour, together with its meaning, is lost to us we can still find echoes of their love of colour in the modern environment. For example, the Hoover Building in Middlesex stands as a 1930s 'temple' to vacuum cleaners. Like the Parthenon its use of white symbolises purity, but this time it refers to the purity of a dirt-free carpet. Meanwhile, the reds, greens, blues and gold which decorate its entrance are borrowed from an ancient

Egyptian decoration. Another modern 'temple' stands in Paris. This is the Pompidou Centre with its red, blue and green columns of ducting on the east elevation. However, unlike the red painted columns on the Minoan palace at Knossus which denote the strength of this supporting element, the hues of the Pompidou Centre are used to colour code the contents of the duct work.

Colours are not only used to paint large and institutional buildings, they are also used to decorate our homes. Here, perhaps, we still use a colour language that is as old as the buildings of antiquity.

Edouard Lovoit's stunning watercolour of a detail of the Parthenon painted at the Ecole des Beaux Arts between 1879–81. Although inaccurate in terms of the extent of its decoration, Lovoit's speculative version of the temple is closer to the truth than our modern view of its white, unpainted marble.

Terraces

Just like traditional Greek houses this street in Toxteth, Liverpool has an annual face-life with a new coat of paint. This redecoration represents a kind of rebirth in which colour plays a key role in simultaneously expressing the individual personalities of the residents within a social cohesion.

Typical of many residential streets in Britain is a series of turn-of-the-century terraced dockers' cottages which run down to the River Mersey in Toxteth, Liverpool. These housefronts have always been well-painted, the pride of the residents being reflected in their façades. The bright and cheerful colours have attracted television film-makers with several productions, including Alan Bleasdale's *Boys from the Blackstuff* and Carla Lane's *Bread*.

So why do the Toxteth householders paint their houses these colours? The first reason is, of course, to give an added protection from the elements. But there are other reasons. Like many other houses all over Britain, paint is used in Toxteth to stamp individuality of ownership. Being architecturally identical to the house next door, each façade is transformed in colour by the personality of its occupants. This colour message is particularly strong on front doors where quite different hues used along the street reflect a communal kaleidoscope of personality. Meanwhile, the more subtle colour differences between each individual façade seem to show respect to their neighbours up and down the street. Overall, the housefront hues suggest not only a harmony of colour, but also social and residential harmony.

However, if we take a closer look at these colours we find another reason for their use. Many of these painted brick houses use red paint to exaggerate the natural colour of brick, while others, possibly in search of status, have painted theirs the colour of stone. This latter use of colour is interesting because it also preoccupied the ancient builders, who used paint to alter the impression of a building material. For example, the ancient Greeks would paint their marble statues flesh pink in order to bring them to life.

A further function of the colours of Toxteth involves a need to define territorial ownership. This is expressed in the meticulously painted boundary lines which signal the edges between one housefront and another. In reflecting two different households, this colour division is often seen on semi-detached houses which, being designed as one building to house two families, is split assunder with two contrasting hues. In Toxteth this boundary line will occasionally be signalled by a shared downspout. In these cases it is not uncommon to find the pipe painted in two colours, each colour representing half-ownership by the house each side.

This language of colour is applied to domestic houses all over the world. Indeed, the traditional colours of houses in parts of Italy, Mexico and Greece and so on, are famous both for their brightness and their spontaneity. However, the fact that house colours can dramatically change from culture to culture and from place to place leads us to an important consideration.

The housepainting tradition in Burano, Italy is striking both in its colour intensity and in its variety. Here, while white frames signal entrances and windows, rich facade hues denote territorial boundaries, an individual colour expression and an overall social harmony.

The colour of place

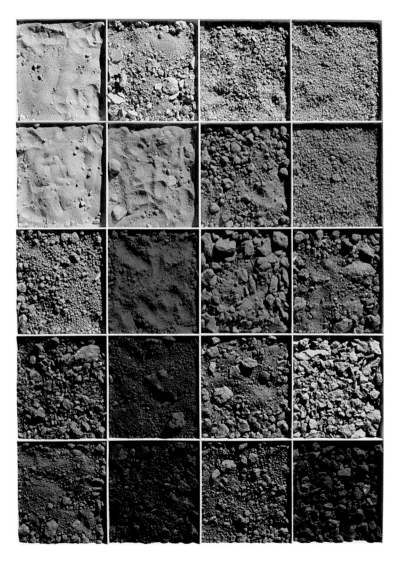

Historically, our towns and cities have been built from local materials and, up to the beginning of the 19th century, were painted with pigment made from local deposits of earth. More vivid paints, such as lime green, Prussian blue and vermilion, could cost up to one hundred times more than the local pigments. Therefore, these colours became the preserve of the rich and, used on housefronts, signalled status and class.

In the countryside, farm buildings were generally painted with the local pigments. This practice caused two basic strategies of decoration. On the one hand, when an earth pigment such as yellow ochre was used, the building would be camouflaged in the same colour as the earth on which it stood. On the other hand, if whitewash was used, the resulting contrast with the landscape would clearly identify the building.

The fact that the traditional colour of settlements seems to communicate a particular 'sense of place' was noted in France by Jean Philippe Lenclos. He noticed that the colours used to paint doors and window shutters in stone-built towns veered toward whites, off-whites and soft greys; colours used in brick-built towns tended to be richer in greens, blues and blue-greens. This observation led

Therefore, the next time you plan to redecorate your housefront, and you wish to remain in keeping with your neighbourhood, you could try a small-scale version of the Lenclos process of environmental colour analysis. This begins with collecting a small range of soil samples from around your area. While doing so you should also gather small flakes of the predominant building materials traditionally associated with your region. Using your set of collected samples as a guide, check their colours against those of an external paint chart. A perfect colour-match with one of your samples is unlikely, so choose a paint colour that is sympathetic to the range.

One brand of external masonry paint, Weathershield, is of interest because it was devised in Britain using Lenclos' methods. Weathershield is colour-matched to a companion range of gloss paints, so any ugly pipework or woodwork on your house can be blended into the overall scheme. Alternatively, details on your housefront can be picked out in white or in a lighter or darker version of the chosen façade colour.

Lenclos suggests that the colour of your front door could also make a colour reference to its local setting. When preparing colour ranges for doors in the French new towns, Lenclos collected gloss paint samples that matched the colours of local wild flowers.

him to survey the whole of France and, later, to produce regional 'maps' of colour. Each of his maps displayed palettes of colour appropriate to each area and are intended as guidelines for those who, in the face of an invasion from new and 'alien' building materials, wish to preserve their local colour.

Although similar colour maps do not exist in Britain (apart from especially colour-protected areas such as parts of Bath and Oxford), a pattern of traditional house colours does exist. For example, in a rural British Isles, our national palette contains 'Suffolk Pink' in the east and some red in the west and umbers to the north and south surrounding a Midlands of yellow ochre.

ABOVE: *Unlike modern architecture which uses 'imported' and synthetic materials, traditional architecture simply utilised natural materials found in the immediate area of the building site.*

LEFT: *Samples of earth collected by Jean Philippe Lenclos. These became the basis of a site-related colour palette.*

Colour psychology

When we enter the front door of our home, we enter a private domain filled with the hues of our choice. But what effect do these colours have on the way we think and feel? Much research has been carried out on the way the colours of rooms might influence us. The following is a brief review of findings in relation to the basic hues:

Red is generally considered to be an arousing and advancing hue. People tend to judge red-painted rooms as smaller than they really are. Red is also a hue much used by interior designers to increase comfort levels in unheated spaces. One Norwegian experiment confirms that when people are put in red or blue rooms of exactly the same temperature, those in the blue room tend to set their thermostats four degrees higher than those in the red room. Red is a good hue for dining spaces. Red and pink are often found in restaurants, especially fast-food restaurants. One study shows that red-stimulated diners tend to eat more quickly and move on for the next person. The prevalence of pink bedrooms has been linked to a study in which Baker-Miller Pink (named after the researchers) was found to have a dramatically calming effect. Meanwhile, the late colour consultant Faber Birren pointed

LEFT: *An experiment conducted by Dr Byron Mikellides at Lund University in Sweden to examine the comparative effect of red and blue painted rooms on heart-rate and brain waves.*

BELOW: *While the Huddersfield Police experiment with the reported subduing effect of a 'Passive Pink' painted holding cell, many detention centres, such as Featherstone Prison, stick with the traditional idea of green as a calming hue.*

to the welcoming effect of a red-yellow and, consequently, recommended it for use in entrance halls.

Purple, for most people, seems a disturbing and psychologically 'difficult' hue for rooms. In a Swedish study purple was voted the most disliked colour in terms of environmental settings.

Blue is considered a passifying and calming hue and has been used in hospitals, particularly in cardiac units. Blue is also understood to have a recessive influence on the appearance of a room's size. For this reason NASA used a grey-blue for the interior of Skylab in order to visually expand the impression of its confined interior. This psychological link between blue and increased space is also applied in countless small and earth-bound rooms.

Green is widely believed to be a calming hue. Indeed, a soothing green paintwork was used in Victorian hospital wards and is also traditionally associated with theatrical Green Rooms where actors relax before making a stage entrance. Moreover, a blue-green was introduced into solitary confinement cells by the last warden of Alcatraz. Greens and, especially, blue-greens are found to enhance both our appetite and the sight of food and are, therefore, another good choice for dining areas.

Yellow finds conflicting research responses. For instance, some clinicians and art therapists find this hue a stressful stimulant and point to the excessive use of yellow in the paintings of the mentally disturbed. Meanwhile, other studies suggest that its stimulation makes it an ideal hue for rooms like studies, where we want to concentrate the mind. Many people use yellow in kitchens and bathrooms to 'cheer themselves up', but one researcher says that if we use strong yellow we are likely to get 'stressed up'.

A further aspect of our experience of colour is the type of light under which hues are viewed. For instance, a blue seen under sunlight in Greece will appear quite different from the same blue viewed under sunlight in Britain. Similarly, inside our houses, different types of electric light will cause the same hue to appear differently (see page 53).

Colour and electric light

Until the advent of gaslight at the beginning of the 20th century the orange glow from candles and oil lamps was the only means of extending daylight and, indeed, the ability to work beyond dusk. Gas mantles were quickly superseded by electric filament bulbs whose harsh and searching light came, not only to extend the working day, but also to cause new attitudes to interior decoration. The widespread use of electric light in the 1930s made homes brighter, and the filament bulb exposed grime previously unseen in gloomier illumination. Kitchens, often the most depressing room in the house, were suddenly transformed into colourful workrooms where drab browns and greens gave way to a white and cheerful paintwork. Colour was now applied to *show* rather than hide the dirt!

However, colour schemes of the time were often gaudy – a brashness induced by the light of electric bulbs. This resulted from the fact that different types of electric light give off slightly different forms of coloured light which alter the colour of rooms they illuminate. We experience these differences of coloured light in sunlight, its changing direction offering a pinkish light at dawn, a yellowish light in daytime and a reddish glow at dusk. However, apart from the angle of sunlight and the prevailing atmospheric conditions, another factor is the point in time that colours are viewed. Along a seasonal cycle, the colours of a landscape will appear quite different in the cold light of winter when compared with those under a summer sun.

We can attune to minor colour shifts using a visual and mental process called 'colour constancy'. This aspect of our colour vision allows the familiar colours of objects, such as a bowl of oranges, to retain their 'normal' colour appearance despite changes in the colour of the light source. But there are occasions when colours which seem correct in one setting appear 'wrong' when viewed in another. This is emphasised in photographs taken under fluorescent light that, when compared with those taken in sunlight, appear colour distorted. Similarly, a comparison of different types of electric lighting reveals a wide variation in colour rendering. For example, a red viewed under tungsten light appears orange while the same red under white fluorescent tubes looks bluish and turns magenta. When the red is subjected to yellowish sodium street lamps it appears as a brown, and when viewed in the greenish light from mercury lamps it turns black.

A comparative sequence of pictures that illustrate the varying colour-rendering characteristics of different light sources.
TOP: *The 'natural' quality of daylight.*
MIDDLE: *The yellow-orange effect of tungsten lighting.*
BOTTOM: *The bluish tinge of 'cool' fluorescent lighting.*

Likewise, the hue of our skin will alter in differently colour rendered settings. For instance, under tungsten light, a warm colour scheme as well as our skin will appear enriched and enhanced; under a blue tinted light, such as white fluorescent, a cool blue or green scheme will be enhanced but our complexion will appear deathly (see page 53).

Therefore, when choosing colours for decoration it is important to know the type of illumination under which both the intended colour scheme *and* the complexion of people will be seen. One paint manufacturer has anticipated this need by installing lighting booths in which large samples of their colour range are presented. At the flick of a switch the colours can be judged under three different types of electric light. However, before buying the chosen tins of paint it would be wise to place both your hands under the light in order to judge their complexion in relation to the selected colour.

Colour and personality

*The eight colours used
in the Max Lüscher
Colour Test.*

If the quality of light represents an external influence on our colour vision, then our own personality represents an internal and private influence on colour choice. But how does colour relate to our personality?

Among the many colour personality tests The Lüscher Colour Test is the most famous. Personality profiles are drawn from a complex sequence of colour selections. Selecting groups and orders then provide the basis for an 'in depth' psychological survey. However, as an introduction to the test and also as an introduction to your own personality according to Lüscher, choose the colour you like best from the series shown here and then refer to the appropriate description. Lüscher asks that, rather than associate colour selection with an object, you should choose the colour for its own sake.

1 Green: the blue-green used in the test is an expression of firmness and constancy and, above all, resistance to change. Those who place green in first position want to assert their self-esteem. They do this by projecting an idealised picture they have of themselves or by seeking recognition. This need to impress is expressed in a quest for better conditions or a longer and more useful life, both for themselves and for others.

2 Red: those who place red in first place display an urge to achieve success and a desire for excitement through those things which offer intensity of living and richness of experience. Red is impulse and the will-to-win in all aspects of living. These desires are reflected in a need for action, a competitive edge and an enterprising productivity.

3 Brown: whoever places brown in first position puts great importance on the need for family security; on hearth and home and the company of one's own kind. Brown also represents physical needs. It is sensuous in its search for security, contentment and the need for creature comforts.

4 Grey: those who favour grey need to insulate themselves from outside influences. Grey is the colour of non-involvement, of those who stand back and watch themselves go through the motions. In other words, grey represents a shield behind which the personality is concealed.

5 Blue: people who favour blue want a calm and orderly environment. This points to a need for traditional settings in which events run smoothly and are free from disturbance. Blue denotes the need for both emotional harmony and a need for bodily rest and contentment. This implies calmness of spirit and a concern that the business of living is dealt with ethically and with integrity.

6 Yellow: if yellow is chosen in first place it shows the desire for change and the hope of greater happiness. This hope is always directed toward the future. Yellow expresses a desire to go forward toward the new, the modern, and the developing. The 'yellow personality' wants to achieve importance. But, unlike green, which is proud and self-contained, yellow is restless in its pursuit of its ambitions.

7 Violet: this colour combines the impulsive vitality of red with the gentle surrender of blue. According to Luscher, violet represents a mystical union in which desires and dreams need to be fulfilled. Therefore, the 'violet personality' wants to charm and delight others, and to exert a degree of fascination over them.

8 Black: being the clour of ultimsate surrender, black functions as a resounding 'no'. Those who choose black in first position want to renounce existing conditions in which he or she feel that nothing is as it should be. The black personality is in the process of stubborn revolt against the direction of its fate.

However, as colours are rarely seen in isolation, we next turn to ways in which they can be combined.

Colour harmony

A 'neutral' colour scheme involving a range of browns and beiges. Although not strictly neutral, such interior schemes provide gentle and restful colour ranges that work well with most light conditions and styles of room.

Choosing colours that go well together does not come naturally to everyone. For instance, if we introduce too many colours, a room may appear hectic and uncoordinated. If we introduce too few colours, a room can look coordinated but appear dull. There are some colour schemes many people find comfortable, schemes that do not irritate or disturb. We call these colour ranges harmonious, balanced or pleasing, and by following some simple rules of harmony we can create successful colour schemes.

The first kind of colour harmony is found extensively in nature such as in the varying shades of green foliage. It is known as a **monochrome**, or one-hue harmony. One-hue harmony combines colours derived from a single hue and, as such, contains a guaranteed degree of success for the home decorator. When developing single hue colour ranges it is important to choose a hue that complements any existing furnishings in the room. It is also important to choose a blend of colours that provide gradual steps of contrast between light and dark tones and between muted and more intense colours. This arrangement of tonal and colour strength allows us to put the colour scheme to work within the room, each colour being used in different quantities to play different roles within the overall scheme. For example, the palest colours can be used for the reflective surfaces of ceiling and walls while, if not the same colour, skirting boards, doors and frames can be contrasted using a slightly lighter or darker colour. Meanwhile, richer colours in the scheme should be reserved for picking out attractive details in the room such as alcoves, beadings and dado rails.

Monochrome schemes are distinctly warm or cool in nature. Of the warmer

harmonies, a neutral colour scheme involving beiges, coffees and browns is among the most popular in use today. Although not strictly neutral, these schemes comprise gentle and restful colour ranges that blend well with most lighting conditions and styles of room. As shown here, they can also be cooled with the addition of the true neutrals – white, grey and black.

The second kind of colour harmony is an **analogous** or related harmony.

Related harmonies are made up from small 'families' of hue, that is, hues that lie next to each other on the colour circle (see pages 12–13). Each of the colour schemes illustrated here derive from related colour pairs, and all can be used with a degree of confidence. However, in order to exercise colour contrast, we should select gradual steps of tone and colour intensity between the colours – the greater the contrast, the bolder and more visually exciting the resulting scheme.

Three related colour harmonies comprising hues found next to each other on the colour circle.

Contrast harmony

Contrasting harmonies create colour schemes which are full of visual spice. The excitement level can be reduced by using either complementary hue in small amounts as an accent hue to enliven the other.

The third method of creating harmonious colour schemes is, possibly, the most exciting of all. This type of harmony is often used to bring a colour scheme vividly to life. For instance, if a living-room is decorated in a restful scheme comprising neutral beiges and terracotta, it can appear twice as effective if highlighted with a touch of lime green or turquoise. A small dash of blue within a bedroom scheme comprising yellows and pinks can become a visual delight. **Contrast harmony** is used by those who prefer a higher degree of stimulation in the home than the visual security offered by related colour harmonies.

This use of colour to accent and emphasise a related family of colour is called **contrast harmony**. Accent colours are simply complementary hues and these are found by looking directly across the colour circle from the chosen sector of related colours (see pages 12–13 and 48). The complementary hue is then introduced into the scheme in small amounts, either to pick out attractive details or to target important objects within the room. Accent colours provide a touch of spice – a heightened colour sensation in which the visual experience of both related colours and accent hue are intensified. When using painted accents in a colour scheme only use a few in any room. Otherwise, they will take over and upset the balance of the overall scheme. Each of the contrast harmonies illustrated here demonstrates the vibrant effect resulting from a balanced use of this exciting colour relationship.

Accents can be introduced without a use of paint. For example, the introduction of green plants to accent a pink-painted room or red roses to accent a soft green room are ways of providing an instant, heightened brilliance. Accent colours can also be introduced in the form of loose furnishings, such as rugs, curtains, lampshades or duvets.

A more dramatic version of the contrast harmony uses a full-blooded version of complementary colour pairs. These are high-contrast schemes which exploit the various strengths and tones of two colours found opposite each other on the colour wheel, such as red and green, blue and orange or yellow and violet. These schemes appeal to the more adventurous decorator but can be tricky and need to follow certain rules. When planning a high-contrast scheme for a room you need to tone down one or all of the colours, or to separate them with a related colour or with neutrals such as grey or white (see page 49). To achieve success you should also remember to vary the amounts and strengths of the complementary colours, and to make sure that no individual colour dominates.

Four examples of contrast harmonies, i.e. related harmonies enlivened with the introduction of a complementary, or accent hue. The complementary hue is shown at the front of each colour scheme.

Colour and proportion

Research into the effects of colour on the visual size of rooms has recently been conducted in Sweden. This work begins to question the popular belief that cool hues, such as blues and greens, cause walls to recede and that warm hues, such as red and yellow, cause walls to advance. For example, look at the end walls in the two rooms shown here. Which wall appears nearer or bigger, the blue wall or the pink wall? The Swedish research emphasises the effect of saturation (colour strength) and tonal value (lightness) as the major influences on the manner in which colour can change the appearance of the proportion of a room.

The best way of looking at this is to imagine a room as it would appear in a black and white photograph. In this mental picture, the importance of colour-tone becomes evident when we compare our experience of tone in a landscape with that of a room. Outdoors, a feeling of verticality or being 'right-way-up' is expressed in the pull of gravity towards the dark tone of the ground against the middle-tones of the distant horizon below the light tones of the sky overhead. This tonal representation of stability is also found in traditionally decorated rooms where floors and carpets are generally darker in tone than surrounding mid-

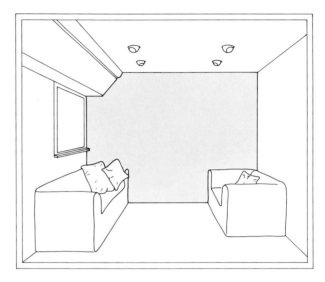

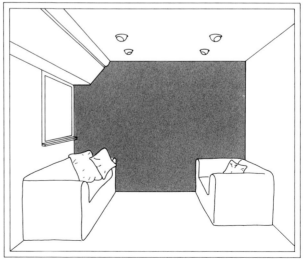

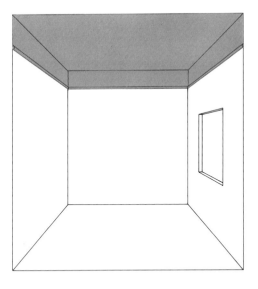

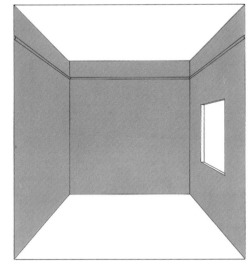

toned walls under light coloured ceilings.

If we change this normal arrangement of tone we can play visual tricks that can alter the proportional appearance of a room. For example, if we paint the ceiling a dark colour and walls a light colour, a tall room will appear wider and lower. This illusion is emphasised if the colour of the ceiling is the same hue as a dark carpet, and also if the ceiling colour is painted down to picture rail level. By reversing this principle, that is, a light coloured ceiling above darker coloured walls, the room will appear taller.

We can make long and narrow rooms, such as corridors and hallways, appear wider by painting the two end walls a dark colour. This illusion is intensified if we decorate the two long walls a light tone. Moreover, painting the ceiling white will increase the amount of reflected light in the room and, thereby, increase its sense of spaciousness.

As a basic rule, small rooms decorated in the palest, lightest colours will enhance the feeling of spaciousness – the greater the lightness and the greater the desaturation, the more distant the surfaces will appear. Equally, we can make large and lofty rooms appear smaller and more intimate by using rich and dark-toned colours on floors, walls and ceiling.

Therefore, before deciding upon a colour scheme you should first assess the shape of the room to be decorated.

Colour interaction and colour size

Two further aspects of colour behaviour should be considered before making final decisions about a decorating scheme.

The first is the effect of colour interaction, that is the way in which a hue will appear to change when seen in the company of different coloured backgrounds (see page 48). This dynamic occurs when, say, a red appears to modify its appearance when seen against a green, and again when seen against a blue. All colours seen in combination are modified in a similar fashion, for instance, red-violet appears more red on a blue background and more blue on a red background. This changing relationship between colours can affect our judgement when we choose paints from small samples on the colour card. The colour appearance of a small paint square chosen against a background of all the other sample squares, will not appear in precisely the same way when viewed later on painted walls and seen in context with all the other colours of a room.

One way of overcoming this problem is to follow a procedure used by interior designers. Assemble a board containing small cut-out samples of all the colours – paint, upholstery, fabrics, etc, to be used in a decorating scheme. The sample board will enable you to preview how

An awareness of the changing impression of colour due to its size is important especially when we select paints from the small colour chips on decorator's cards for use on the large walls of a room.

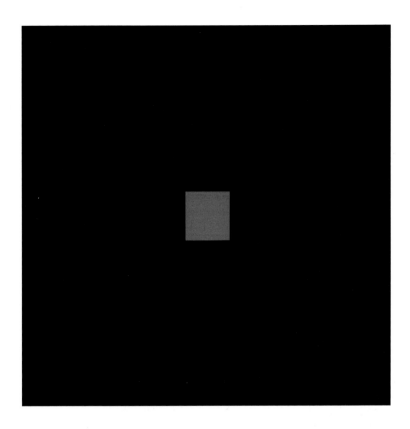

red on the same black background. The smaller amount of red seems to be slightly darker than its counterpart seen in the bigger square. This subtle colour shift is crucial when making decorating decisions because any difference will be amplified when we compare a colour chosen from a small square on the colour card against the same colour painted over the surface area represented by, say, four walls and a ceiling. This increase in the size of a colour causes a corresponding increase in our sensitivity to colour. As a result, a colour can appear to brighten in its effect by up to 50 per cent. Sometimes, therefore, a more muted version of the desired colour might be more likely to achieve the required finished effect.

The modification of colour by its area size and by its juxtaposition with other colours has been anticipated by two of the leading paint manufacturers who market small pots of sample paint called testers. These allow the home decorator to install a trial colour scheme at a size (around one square metre) at which the overall effect of colours can be confidently predicted.

individual hues will behave within the overall colour scheme.

The second aspect of colour worth considering is the changing effect of hues seen at different sizes. For instance, as the area of a colour increases in size it also begins to alter its appearance. Compare the two squares of the same

Colour and style

Cosy, traditional rooms tend to utilise colour and pattern generously across many surfaces, their colours often making direct reference to those found in nature.

The colour scheme that you ultimately choose will respond to the function of the room and its planned style of decoration. Style is an important aspect of decoration because, not only will it reflect the kind of home you live in but it will also relate to your type of lifestyle. For instance, you may live in a new house and decide to create a modern, high-tech style interior

that is a cool and efficient 'machine for living in'. On the other hand, you may live in an older house and choose a period style in which textures and patterns abound. These approaches to decoration are equally valid but each suggest different ways of using colour.

Older houses often contain natural focal points, such as sloping ceilings, wood panelling and ornamental fireplaces, to which the eye is drawn. These features can be highlighted with colour. Around these a period style scheme say, in warm beige and peach accented with pinks or greens, can be developed. The chosen colour theme can also be carried through into the patterns of fabrics and upholstery, bringing a sense of unity. However, in rooms containing many interesting features the use of too many colour ranges should be avoided as they can create too many focal points that compete for attention.

Modern homes tend to be less ornate, even featureless. This gives you the freedom to decorate them in any style that you like. It also provides the necessity for using colour to create a focal point. If you decide on a high-tech scheme, use colours clearly to express the function of the room. For example, modern style rooms often use white, greys and black or

By contrast, modern style interiors reject pattern for a concentration on a functional use of colour and surface. Here colour is used to emphasise the planes of floors, walls and ceilings, and to target the shape of objects and furniture within the room.

neutrals as background wall and ceiling colours, against which stronger hues are reserved for focusing attention on objects within the room. When bold and cheerful colours are introduced these usually draw from the primary and secondary hues. The selected hue is then used to coordinate the colours of blinds, rugs, prints, high-tech furniture or a well-displayed collection of objects.

Whether modern style or period style, the final step is to find your chosen colour scheme in the paint cards. Modern paint manufacturers offer vast ranges of colour all at a similar price. With all these hues at your disposal you might think that picking the right colours to suit your decorating needs is an easy task.

However, many of the retail paint cards show around 70 or so gloss and emulsion colours because these represent the best-selling paints and you may not find the colour you want. If so, ask your supplier for a trade card. Trade paint cards are not confined to professional decorators and, like ICI's 'Colour Dimensions' range, can offer up to 2,000 hues. Although extensive, even these ranges cannot hope to provide all the colours of the rainbow. If you still fail to find the precise colours that you want, another option is turn to the specialist paintmakers who not only provide alternative colour ranges but will also mix paint to precisely match a colour sample provided by the customer. Happy decorating!

WEARING COLOUR: *Colour distinctions*

In the biological records of animal life it is apparent that the female responds to vivid colours. Evidence of this is found among birds, fish and animals where the male of the species, such as the peacock and the drake, are brightly coloured to attract a mate. Meanwhile, the female of the various species is often coloured in neutral greys or browns, possibly to provide a protective camouflage when producing and rearing her young.

Throughout human history the colour of clothing has been invested with magical and mystical meanings and it has always been used to create an artificial distinction between the sexes. For instance, the ancient Persians used a law to restrict the number of colours in women's dress. Similar codes of dress restricting women's colours to drab greens and browns were also introduced in ancient Greece and during the Roman Empire. An early Christian edict pronounced that the female form should be hidden from view in undyed materials because colour was 'unnecessary to health', was 'false', and 'afflicted greedy eyes'. Furthermore, '... God would have sheep purple if He wished the woollen clothes to be purple'.

Historically, colour was also used to distinguish between the classes. Such colour discrimination between sex and class amongst the masses was still active during the reigns of Henry VIII and Elizabeth I – neither of whom are remembered for the dullness of their dress.

Much of our present formality of dress results from these restrictions: the white and veiled bridal gown representing purity; a respectful black worn by widows and by mourners, and the use of purple by religious leaders and royalty.

A sexual colour coding still survives today. Babies still being dressed in pink for a girl and blue for a boy. This tradition may have originated in ancient Egypt, where boys were seen as a gift from the heavens, and so became associated with blue, while girls were seen as being of the flesh and were, therefore, invested with a more mortal skin colour. Also, the Victorian class division of 'blue collar worker' and 'white collar worker' is still in common currency.

The gradual breakdown of these colour distinctions in dress has given way to the rise of individuality and its colour expression in clothes.

Set against the historical background of colour restriction in women's clothes, red has been associated by men with harlots in red light districts and with 'scarlet women'. Today, red is a high-fashion colour and enjoys a seasonal popularity, particularly at Christmas-time.

Colour and self-image

Generally speaking, we wear the colours in which we feel most comfortable and that reflect our general outlook on life. As well as responding to inward needs, our colour decisions for clothes have to work in relation to our complexion and colouration. This results in a highly complicated colour signalling language. For example, vivid colours worn by extroverted people to project an outgoing personality can also be worn by introverted people who wish to disguise a shy and retiring personality.

Contrary to the advice of some fashion experts, women who feel themselves to be overweight will often wear black. In principle this illusion seems to work. For example, hold this page away at arm's length and view the two dresses shown here. The darker dress does appear the smaller of the two, even when the page is turned sideways or upside down.

According to studies in Poland and America, the habitual wearing of black and dark clothes, to the exclusion of other colours, can denote depression. One psychiatrist, Dr Jean Rosenblaum, an expert in self-image, has even gone as far as to suggest that this might also hide an emotional problem. He advises that when we are depressed and wear dark and neutral clothes, we should change

Some women wear black to create the illusion of appearing slimmer. Compare the colours of these two dresses and see if you agree with this belief.

into brighter colours, concluding that we will be 'amazed at what colour does for our spirits'. This transformation of spirit is echoed by fashion designers who suggest that we behave and even walk differently when dressed in black compared with, say, red.

Our self-image is improved if we feel that our skin looks healthy. A radiant glow of health can be induced by using colour. The classic example of skin colour emphasis is the sight of a glowing golden sun tan in a blue blouse or shirt. The 'glow' is often an illusion caused by a complementary colour contrast in which blue, the opposite hue of yellow-orange on the colour circle, intensifies the golden hue of the skin. Another way of improving pale complexions is the wearing of red scarves and red sweaters as red reflects a warm glow back onto the face. Conversely, it has been suggested that a greenish blue scarf or sweater will tone down a ruddy complexion.

Two colour systems have been devised that claim to help us make the appropriate decisions when it comes to clothes and make-up. Both are based on simple tests that aim to determine our colour type and both are reviewed on the following pages.

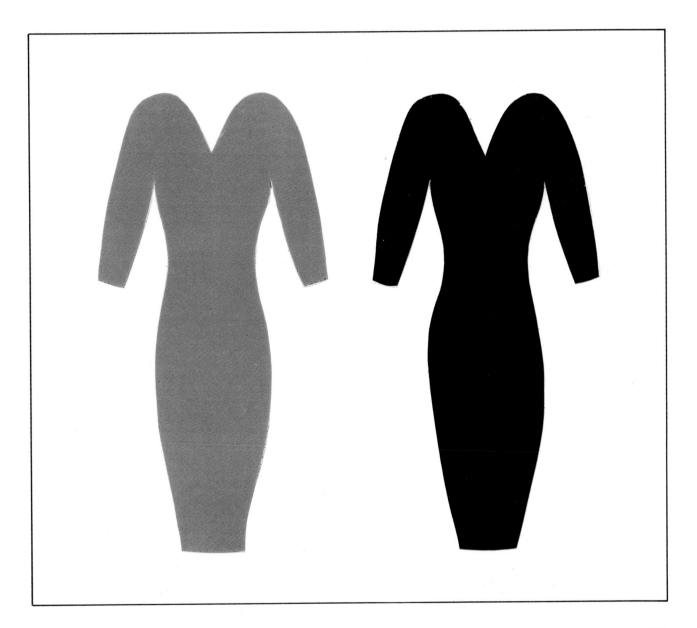

Colour and beauty

There are two popular methods of colour analysis in use that claim to help people build up an accurate picture of themselves in terms of the colours they wear. Both methods focus on finding our colour 'look' as the key to the successful projection of beauty, perspective of life and the overall impression we make on others.

The Colour and Style File

This is based on the premise that we each display an individual hair, eye and skin colouration that corresponds to six primary characteristics. They are: dark, light, bright, muted, warm or cool.

The identification of our primary colour-tone characteristic together with a secondary colour-tone characteristic is the main point of the analysis. For example, a 'dark' person can have a secondary characteristic of 'bright' or 'muted' and a 'muted' person can exhibit secondary characteristics which might be 'dark' or 'light'. This duality of primary and secondary colour-tone characteristics is, according to its authors, what gives us our uniqueness in colour.

The analysis begins by identifying our most dominant colour type. This is done by looking at ourself in the mirror and asking 'What do I see first?' Do you see

yourself as 'dark' or 'light', 'bright' or 'muted', or 'warm' or 'cool'? As a rough guide, 'darks' will have deep colouring with dark hair and dark eyes, while 'lights' tend to be naturally blonde or ash blonde with little contrast between hair and skin. 'Brights' have high contrast colouring, while 'muted' people seem to have unrelated groups of body colours

This sequence of colour fans are devised by the Academy of Colour and Style as hues both for determining your own basic colour characteristic and for

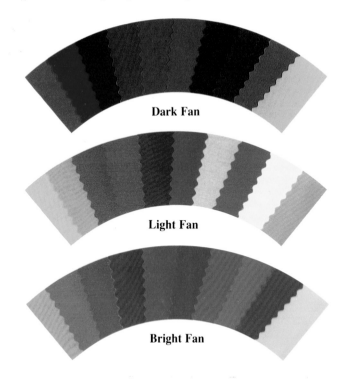

Dark Fan

Light Fan

Bright Fan

such as warm coloured hair and a cool coloured skin. 'Warm' people literally radiate warmth through hair, eyes and skin, while 'cool' people have cool-looking eyes and skin – a cool type often being recognised by a loss of hair pigmentation.

Confirmation of our colour type is gained by looking at the six colour fans illustrated here and eliminating those that seem inappropriate. By concentrating upon those fans remaining, you should be able to identify your primary colour-tone characteristic. If further confirmation is required, you are advised to visit your local fabric shop and experiment with colours drawn from those fans you are left with. To do so, you should compare different colours, that is, drape a colour-matched red from one fan over one shoulder, and drape a red derived from another fan over the other shoulder. This comparative process continues until you have, by elimination, identified your colour type. Once identified, you have not only found your main characteristic but you have also found the colours of clothes that will look best on you.

The second part of **The Colour and Style File** method turns to finding your secondary colour-tone characteristic. This is achieved using the same methods already described. Once this is isolated, you emerge as a 'bright-dark' or a 'light-muted' etc. This knowledge then releases an even wider range of colours (not shown here) comprising fans of hues and neutrals that complement your colour-tone personality.

illustrating ranges of colour that best suit your type of colouration. The fans below represent the six main tonal types.

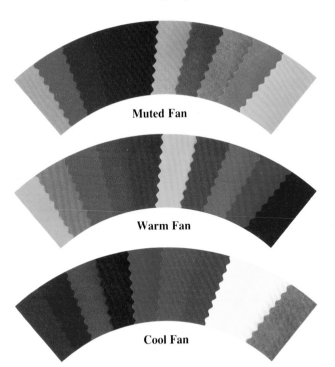

Muted Fan

Warm Fan

Cool Fan

Colour Me Beautiful

This theory claims to help us become experts on our own personal use of colour through an analysis test known as **Colour Me Beautiful**. The test was borrowed from the writings of the German Bauhaus design school teacher and colour expert Johannes Itten (see page 12). He noticed that the colours used by his students in their paintings were invariably complementary to the hues of their own skin, hair and eyes.

The test sets out to discover your own personal inclination toward certain groups of colours and, from these, to identify your colour type. Colour types are described in terms of 'seasons'. Once identified, the associated 'seasonal' colour palette then becomes a personal guide to the colours you should wear, as these colours will best project your own colouration. The first part of the test is divided into two steps.

Step One is to identify the key colours you have consistently and successfully worn in the past. To do this, study the lists shown here and pick the group containing the most colours that seem to have brought you more compliments in your life. Although each of the groups may contain colours that you already wear or have worn, the test reminds you to ask yourself, 'Which group is the best for me?' This step is intended to discover your inclination toward either 'warm' or

Determining your season opens the door to a palette of colour for clothes that fit your colouring. Spring's colours are delicate or bright with yellow undertones (spring people include Margaret Thatcher and Nancy Reagan). Autumn's colours are richer with orange and gold undertones (autumn people include Vanessa Redgrave and Glenda Jackson). Winter's colours are clear, vivid, or icy, with blue undertones (winter people include Elizabeth Taylor and Virginia Wade). And summer's colours are cool and soft with blue undertones (summer people include Princess of Wales and Penelope Keith).

'cool' colours.

Step Two takes you to the colour charts on the right. Using your 'warm' and 'cool' classification as a guide, explore the relevant seasonal colour palettes and choose your personal colour range. This now decides whether you are a 'winter', 'summer', 'autumn' or 'spring' person.

A second part of the test evaluates your skin tone and is intended to confirm the colour decision made in the first part of the analysis. This stage involves looking at yourself in a mirror under natural light and identifying your skin tone. As the skin acts as a colour filter, its tone lies just below the surface and, according to **Colour Me Beautiful**, identification of your skin tone is the key to knowing the colours that best suit you. For example, 'summer' and 'winter' types have blue-pink skin undertones; 'autumn' and 'spring' types have golden undertones.

If your skin tone is subtle you are advised to try comparing your wrists and palms with others to see if you are more 'blue' than 'golden'.

The third stage in the analysis continues with check lists for hair and eye colours and helps those who are unsure by draping different coloured fabrics around the neck and shoulders. Those who have determined their colour 'season' are encouraged to accept the whole palette as the basis for their future wardrobe.

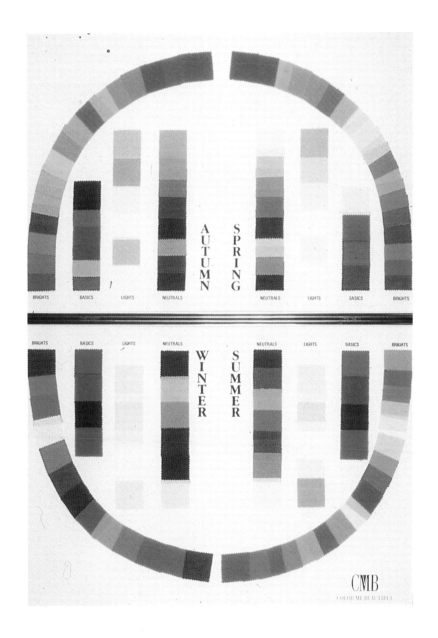

Colour and make-up

LEFT: *From the earliest times a white painted face has been viewed by women as desirable. In some primitive tribes the whitewashed faces of young girls represents purification and a coming of age. The cosmetic white face is an important aspect of traditional geisha make-up and it also found favour with Elizabeth I and with Hollywood stars. While symbolising virtue and innocence, facial whiteness also provides a contrasting background against which the dark delineation of eyes and redness of lips are emphasised.*

RIGHT: *Modern trends in make-up constantly explore new combinations and unusual colour effects such as glitter and metallic sheen. This responds both to the seasons of the year and to different customer outlooks in style. According to make-up artist B. J. Gillian the old rules of colour co-ordination have gone. She says: 'It is no longer a case of everything being matt or your eyeshadow toning in with your lipstick. What makes a face look modern is a touch of incongruity.'*

The modification of the natural appearance of the face using colour has a long history. Indeed, this use of facial pigment can be traced back to the earliest cultures. In his book, *Manwatching*, Desmond Morris writes that the larger, fleshier lips of the female have always 'been further magnified in size, colour and texture by the application of lip-

stick – a practice known to be at least 4000 years old'.

This language of facial colour also has links with the colour signalling used by birds and mammals in the wild. Redness is a common courtship signal among several mammals and birds. We too can biologically communicate redness with the raising of blood to the surface of our skin when blushing or the reddening and swelling of our lips when sexually aroused.

The application of artificial colour to the face transfixes these signals and exaggerates features so that they can be projected over a greater distance. Degrees of colour exaggeration can vary from culture to culture and will also change in response to fashion. An Elizabethan fashion for a white painted face contrasting with reddened lips was created by Elizabeth I. Later, during the seventeenth and eighteenth centuries, both men and women used excessive make-up, but this fashion waned during a superficially puritanical Victorian period. A revival came in the early twentieth century with the development of synthetic colourants combined with the influence of Hollywood stars such as June Harlow and Claudette Colbert. Today, fashions in make-up are more transient and tend to be used to subtly enhance a natural look rather than create an artificial illusion of beauty.

Degrees of power dressing

According to Carlton Wagner, the American colour consultant, there is no one correct colour for business attire. However, he does suggest that certain colours can play positive roles in the office and can also draw different responses when dealing with colleagues, clients and customers. Therefore, he proposes that, if we are to be effective in our work, we should understand the impression the colours of our business dress can create.

Wagner proposes that the ultimate colours for authority are a black suit, a white shirt or blouse with a small amount of red – worn as a tie, wrap, pocket handkerchief or button-hole. This combination represents the colours of the 'power dresser' in the business world. Wagner adds that the power colours can also work against the wearer and should be used with care. These are not the colours to wear when applying for a new job, nor if your business role involves gaining information from others as they appear too intimidating. They are most appropriate to the high-powered decision-maker who will not take 'no' for an answer. These are also the colours, for firing people, for those who wear them are less likely to be contradicted.

Some fashion pundits suggest that we project different personas and are treated differently when wearing different coloured clothes. For instance, the black formal business suit – when worn with white and red – is regarded as the apparel of the ambitious power dresser, giving the wearer a competitive edge over his or her colleagues.

Which of the suit colours shown here would you wear in each of the following situations? For example, when applying for a job; when selling merchandise, when interviewing people, and for getting along with your colleagues. See if your choices tally with Wagner's recommendations.

Dark blue and dark grey suits are colours that allow others to concentrate on what you have to say rather than what you are wearing. They are the colours traditionally linked with respect and authority and make a good colour choice for drawing positive responses from clients and customers. These colours wear well for interviews and, especially, when promoting new ideas or selling new products (see page 29).

Fawn suits, especially when worn with a soft blue shirt or blouse, represent less of a threatening colour choice. These are colours to wear if you wish clients and colleagues to communicate freely with you. In other words, these colours are good for interviewing people; they represent professionalism without causing any inhibition in those you deal with.

Brown suits are a tricky colour choice in the business world. Wagner says that, although a dark brown suit can make a good alternative to dark blue and dark

What kind of responses do we encourage when we wear suits in the colours shown here? The American colour consultant, Carlton Wagner provides us with some interesting answers.

grey, it exerts no power advantage. When it is dark enough it will allow you equal status with colleagues in the office, but it is definitely not the colour to wear when meeting clients. Furthermore, if brown is tempered with yellow, it becomes the colour of diminished status. It should be avoided if the wearer seeks respect and a degree of authority.

Green suits give an 'off-duty' impression and are not successful as business dress. According to Wagner, green clothes should be confined to a recreational wardrobe together with other less conservative colours.

The colour language of ties

The conventionally dressed man tends to find his colour expression in accent hues – small spots of colour flashed from a pocket handkerchief, from socks and, especially, from a tie. However, as a national survey of tie wearers in the UK discovered, this small area of colour can represent a highly complex signalling system which has some links in the animal kingdom.

The tie survey was carried out in 1989 as part of the *Tie Rack Report* in which over 1,000 men were asked to choose tie colours to suit various formal and informal social occasions. You too can take part in this survey. Look at the ties shown here and make a selection in response to each of the following questions. Which colour of tie would you choose:

The colour of a tie appears to function as a kind of message. When you go for a job interview, go out for a night on the town with boys, or try to impress your work colleagues, a girlfriend or her parents, which colour would you choose?

1 when taking a woman out to dinner for the first time and with whom a serious relationship is intended?
2 when first invited to meet your girlfriend's parents?
3 when going on the town for a night out with male friends?
4 when being interviewed for a new job?
5 when attempting to impress your work colleagues?

The overall response to these and other questions placed the blue tie consistently in first place. The overriding popularity of blue in ties is interesting because it agrees with many other colour preference tests (see pages 150–1). Beyond the popularity of a tranquil blue, it was the changing colour of ties in second place that proved fascinating.

For example, when taking a woman out to dinner for the first time, blue was strongly challenged by red for first place. However, when the same men were asked which colour they would wear when meeting her parents, the red slumped to the bottom of the list to be replaced by the more 'respectable' grey tie.

Redness, in the form of red and pink ties, is a strong contender for second place for going out on the town with male friends. In this setting, red seems to function as an attention grabbing signal – a sign of potency aimed specifically at the opposite sex, and at its strongest among older men.

The meaning of red in ties has echoes in the mating rituals of some animals and birds. For example, when seeking partners both the Anole lizard and the Frigate bird will inflate red throat sacs to send 'come hither' signals. On human males, the red signal can be aimed at a potential mate but *not* at her parents.

When it came to applying for a job, the integrity of a blue tie took an impressive first place with grey in second position. However, when asked which colour tie would impress work colleagues, of those surveyed who said that their main job priority was success, all chose a red silk tie as the emblem of the 'power dresser'. The overriding popularity of blue ties and red ties in these settings holds strong meanings. On the one hand, blue represents integrity, the need to be trusted and the need to be seen as trustworthy by others. On the other hand, the association of sexual prowess with a red tie extends to the search for success and authority.

In response to other questions in the survey, tie colours were also found to be linked with changing seasons; red ties being favoured on cold winter mornings (the warmth of the winter sun?) and yellow ties favoured on hot summer mornings (the colour of the summer

sun?). Hair pigmentation also seemed to influence colour choice. Red-headed men showed the strongest preference for red ties, while blonds seemed more willing to experiment with purples and greens. Meanwhile, dark-haired men constantly preferred blue and red ties, while greying and white-haired men, possibly selecting a hue to compensate for a lost pigmentation, plumped for brown ties.

Both men and women use the colour of dress to either display membership of a social group or to hide in the crowd. Two colours that are commonly enlisted in this function are denim and khaki.

*Native to the southern states of America, the Anole Lizard (*Anolis carolinensis*) uses his inflatable throat sac rather like a red tie to attract and flag down passing females. However, would he use his red 'tie' when meeting his mate's parents?*

Khaki and denim uniforms

The desire to dress in a manner that enables the wearer either to show allegiance to a social group or to fade into a crowd or the landscape has a fascinating background. Two dyes that serve this need are indigo and khaki. Both have connections with warfare, both emerged in the mid 19th century to survive the vagaries of modern fashion and both are colours that have their origins in India.

Khaki began its life in the dust of India. Indeed, the word khaki is the Hindustani word for dust. Its story began in 1846 when Sidney Lumsden, a soldier with the East India Company with a strong instinct for survival, went to battle in his pyjamas which he had dyed the colour of dust. Hitherto, the British Army wore scarlet uniforms, perhaps to appear royal or possibly to camouflage the sight of blood but, essentially, providing a sitting target for the enemy!

Beyond its universal adoption by the world's armies, khaki has also become the uniform of gentry aspiring urban and suburban ruralists. Senior ranks wear the upmarket Burberry raincoat while pretend 'private eyes' and 'news reporters' hide behind the upturned collar of the trenchcoat. When they take to the countryside they deliberately dress down in Barbour all-weather hunting jackets above cow-dung coloured Wellington boots. These are the 'county' colours that express an affinity with nature and membership of an environmentally friendly brigade.

While lower ranks of ruralists go hiking and climbing in khaki walking shorts and jungle hats, more aggressive forms of a camouflage stalk the streets of the city.

Variations of khaki appear on hunting jackets, Wellington boots, Range Rovers and even on Harrods shopping bags to symbolise the County Set who either identify with the land or with the landed gentry.

Here, flak and bush jackets announce the uniform of urban 'Rambos' who wear army surplus battle dress to represent their toughness and readiness for action.

Blue dye was originally processed from the *Indigofera tinctoria* plant which only grows in India (see page 67). It was scarce in medieval Europe and, consequently, blue fabric was highly prized. After the Bavarian tailor Levi Strauss imported the synthetic version of indigo into America in the late 19th century to colour his jeans, the demand for denim soared. Strauss had been using denim for supplying the gold rush miners with tenting and wagon covers but, realising its durability, he began a sideline using offcuts to make work trousers.

What began as overalls for blue collar workers later became the widespread uniform of a middle-class youth. However, as khaki had transcended its militaristic beginnings so, too, blue denim has become completely ageless, sexless, classless and global. Indeed, it is worn by off-duty US presidents and Soviet youths who are willing to give up a month's wages for the privilege.

The faded nature of denim, highly prized among its legions, also has a history. It stems from when indigo provided the deep-sea blue of the Royal Navy uniform, and a faded blue symbolised the veteran.

Denim blue has become the classless uniform of the masses. Faded blue is the prized hue of seasoned jeans. This occurs through washing and also when the upper blue warp begins to wear through to the white weft underside.

All the colours of the world

UNITED COLORS OF BENETTON.

The Benetton design concept of 'all the colours of the world' draws bright ethnic colours from a mixture of Third World cultures. These are then successfully redirected at an international teenage fashion market in the Western world.

Like fine art and design, fashion expresses the spirit of our times. It also reflects our continual search for new colour experiences and, as part of this quest, regularly pops up with vivid colour combinations. It is as though we need from time to time to discover the power of the primary hues as the basis of all colour expression. One such point in time occurred in the post-war affluence of the 1960s when clothes suddenly took on bright and primitive hues (see page 56).

The fascination for brightly coloured clothes came as a reaction to an earlier trend for 'state-of-the-art' coloured materials such as space-age silvery metallics and black plastic. In coinciding with the advent of manned spaceflight and black and white Op art, this earlier trend saw the stark white fashion geometry of Courrèges and Mary Quant's black mini-skirt.

Space-age fantasy was replaced by another form of escapism, this time involving 'trips' into the inner recesses of the mind to experience a rainbow of psychedelic hues. This new quest for self-discovery saw 'Flower Children' travelling to Tibet and Nepal in search of themselves while others took advantage of a booming package holiday industry to seek 'local colour' abroad.

Soon, boutiques, such as Monsoon and Oasis, began importing colourful fabrics and clothes from all over the world and ethnic fashion was born. Today, it is the basis of Benetton's international success in promoting 'all the colours of the world'.

One fashion designer who utilises ethnic influences in her work, is the high priestess of fashion colour, Zandra Rhodes. While Laura Ashley diverted the ethnic trend into the white lace and

Creator of the total colour look including hair, make-up and dress, Zandra Rhodes herself appears as the walking showcase of her colourful creations.

parchment frills of peasant costumery, Rhodes captured the spirit of international colour and elevated ethnic hues to the status of haute couture. Her own fashion approach includes a very personalised approach to make-up, inspired by the 1960s 'hippy' trend in facial decoration, and punk-inspired vividly dyed hair. The result is a look which is pure theatre.

The cinema provides another channel of influence on the colours that we wear. For example, in the early 1970s *The Great Gatsby* launched the pinks and white of the 'Gatsby look'. It also launched the costume designer, Ralph Lauren, to international recognition. Today it is not unusual to find leading international fashion designers involved in major feature films. Jean Paul Gaultier coincided his summer collection with the same clothing he designed for *The Cook, The Thief, His Wife and Her Lover*, while Cerruti was responsible for the wardrobe designs in *The Witches of Eastwick* and *Fatal Attraction*.

While the colours that we choose to wear may be selected to alleviate depression, to boost morale or to influence other people's opinion of us, it is difficult to ignore fashion colours because they dictate what is available in the shops.

COLOUR AND COMMERCE:
Colour and advertising

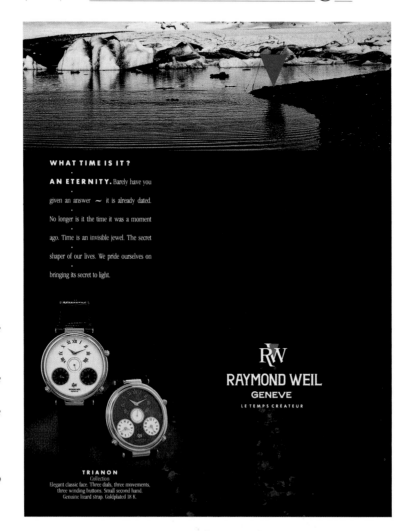

WHAT TIME IS IT?

AN ETERNITY. Barely have you given an answer ∼ it is already dated. No longer is it the time it was a moment ago. Time is an invisible jewel. The secret shaper of our lives. We pride ourselves on bringing its secret to light.

RW

RAYMOND WEIL
GENEVE
LE TEMPS CRÉATEUR

TRIANON
Collection
Elegant classic face. Three dials, three movements, three winding buttons. Small second hand. Genuine lizard strap. Goldplated 18 K.

This magazine ad illustrates two eye-controlling strategies. First, a complementary accent hue draws the eye to the landscape and then links it with the brand name; second, the product is shown in the lower left portion of the composition, a position that, according to research, is precisely where our eyes expect to find important information.

The world of advertising bombards us with a barrage of multi-coloured images from the pages of magazines, our television screens and the hoardings on the walls of cities. This use of colour is very calculated. Advertisers operate from an understanding of how we can be visually and mentally manipulated. As a result of motivational research into our desires and fantasies, and studies using the Eye Movement Recorder (sophisticated equipment that can record the patterns of our eye movement over a page or a screen) merchandisers have learned to communicate with us on both conscious and unconscious planes.

Advertisers know that, compared with black and white imagery, we profoundly respond to coloured pictures. On a conscious level colour conveys a richer degree of information regarding the texture, tangibility and, therefore, accessibility of products. On an unconscious level desirability can be established by using colours that strike chords deep within the inner recesses of our mind.

This deeper response is demonstrated by countless mailshot findings in which dramatically more responses are gained from adverts printed on coloured papers or using colour photographs as compared with those printed on white or neutral paper, or using black and white photographs. Also, coloured adverts in magazines will grab a longer attention span than black and white versions. Most important is that, in similar comparisons, our memory recall from full colour information is far more pronounced.

As a result of the enormous investment in colour advertising, adverts are carefully colour structured to 'take the eye for a walk', or to pull the eye directly to the main message. This involves a skilful use of colour contrast to target the brand name or the image of the product itself. This colour targeting often sees the key words or images of an advert being heightened using complementary hues – an eye-pulling strategy reminiscent of John Constable's spot of red in a green landscape painting (see pages 82–3).

Another colour targeting strategy employs the 'full circle' principle. This arranges spots of the same target or accent hue against strongly contrasting background colours to draw the eye from point to point around the advert before coming to rest on its message area. The message area is that point in the advert at which the 'punchline' is delivered. It is this area that usually coincides with the greatest amount of colour contrast.

Colour and communication

In the world of advertising, colour has more impact than any other sense. Indeed, some adverts rely solely upon colour instantly to communicate their meaning. For example, can you identify the product promoted by these two adverts? Each one represents a highly successful brand campaign and each one also avoids the use of words or a picture of the product to make their point.

At this sophisticated level of communication a colour picture has been used to suggest attributes that the advertisers wish us to associate with the product. In the case of gold, the image promotes our search for wealth and riches and suggests an acquisitive Midas touch. Meanwhile, purple is associated with 'high rank' and exclusivity and, combined with gold and black, is

MIDDLE TAR As defined by H.M. Government
Warning: SMOKING CAN CAUSE LUNG CANCER, BRONCHITIS AND OTHER CHEST DISEASES
Health Departments' Chief Medical Officers

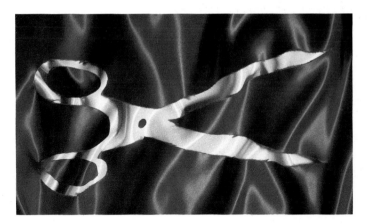

LOW TAR As defined by H.M. Government DANGER: Government Health WARNING: CIGARETTES CAN SERIOUSLY DAMAGE YOUR HEALTH

LEFT AND ABOVE: *These enigmatic but familiar ads use colour rather than words to communicate their message.*

on tropical islands and Marlboro cigarettes on a western prairie.

The immediacy of colour advertising is also exemplified in adverts for painkillers such as Syndol which use red and jagged shapes to suggest pain and smooth blue shapes to suggest relief. In the advert for Inoven, pink lettering on a jarring green background screams: 'Hit pain where it hurts' – a discordant colour message which is, in itself, enough to cause a headache. An empty deep green background of a magazine advert carrying the caption, 'A chameleon on a snooker table next to a cool Gordon's & Tonic with a slice of lime' poses a colour conundrum. However, while momentarily catching our curiosity the green evokes tropical vegetation, humidity and the smell of lime. In each case, colour brings a strong reinforcement to the message, adding a dimension of meaning in which the power of colour is worth a thousand words.

reserved for product promotions which seek association with expensiveness and luxury.

Colour associations can hold a deeper significance. The blueness of lakes and the sea both offer new life and trigger primitive sexual associations. This mental connection accounts for their use as settings for the promotion of products such as Wella shampoo and to launch countless new car models. Another use of colour lures future purchasers by placing the product slightly out of reach. This ploy uses the orange-yellow of beaches and sunsets to entice our imagination to exotic places. This exploitation of colour fantasy sets Bacardi rum and Bounty bars

Colour in the supermarket

As an average UK supermarket stocks around 11,000 different items, colour is enlisted to single out individual products to make them more appealing. Furthermore, as well over half of all supermarket sales are unpremeditated, colour functions as a weapon to encourage the impulse-buying majority.

A closer look at the products and their packaging finds a basic colour language. High legibility hues such as red and yellow flash 'new' and 'improved' messages on packaging, while background colours on products concealed in packets, tins and bottles often use colours to com-

Blue, white and grey are hues used in various combinations to symbolise hygiene and unadulteration. They are used extensively in packaging, especially for white products, and communicate their purity to the consumer.

municate the actual, desired or idealised hues of the unseen product. Colour is enlisted to convey attributes of products that their manufacturers or processors would wish us to associate with them. For instance, various permutations of blue, white and grey are often employed to depict the purity, freshness and unadulteration of various brands of sugar, flour, salt and milk. Adding a touch of red to the package will increase a sense of power, such as with bleach or toothpaste. Greens and yellows project the freshness of vegetables and fruit. Orange, either individually or in the company of other 'power' hues such as dark blue and yellow, signifies a healthy energy when associated with vitamins and breakfast cereals but, when combined with ultramarine, conveys the power to clean the weekly wash.

The package designs illustrated opposite represent a Swiss attempt to determine a common colour language for international marketing. The colour combinations on each package result from market research studying European and American consumers. Before reading on, see if you agree with its findings. Imagine that you are in a supermarket and simply guess at the product you would expect to find inside each packet.

Solution: A washing powder; B cocoa; C disinfectant; D toothpaste; E poison; F cosmetics; G tonic food; H vegetables.

After double-checking this test with Italian, French, British and American subjects certain oddities arise. For instance, the proposed colours for disinfectant (C) can be confused with tooth-

Which product would you expect to find in each of these coloured packages?

paste, while the latter (D) can be interpreted as colours for mineral water or milk. The black and yellow scheme for poison (E) is interesting because they are the colours of caution used on the rear of heavy goods vehicles and trains, and are also found on reptiles and, especially, insects who carry a sting in their tails.

Colour and appetite appeal

During our visit to the supermarket we should also be aware of how much our expectations of highly coloured foodstuffs have affected its preparation. Statistics show that around 200,000 tonnes of additives are consumed each year in the United Kingdom, which amounts to 10 lbs for each adult. Furthermore, $\frac{9}{10}$ of the 3,700 chemical compounds used in the mass marketing of food are used solely for cosmetic purposes. These figures reflect our demand for the 'correct' colour appearance of fruit, vegetables and meat, and respond to our strong associations of bright colour with freshness and flavour.

Certain hues such as red, golden orange and green are known as the 'appetite colours' and these are an important ingredient in the mass marketing of food. For instance, golden brown is so appetising a food colour that the baking of bread and cereals is carefully controlled to achieve precisely the right colour. The yellow dye tartrazine is added to cakes and fish batter for the same purpose. The appetising sight of our morning kipper is another colour illusion as its mouthwatering appearance results from orange dye and its flavour results from being coated in essence of smoke tar. The appearance of butter, if not controlled by a colourant, would resemble lard at low temperatures and, in America, some oranges would appear with mottled green skins if not dipped in dye to achieve an acceptable colour perfection.

Like all frozen vegetables, peas have a natural green that results from being picked prematurely and quickly scalded for the freezing process. Canned peas lose their natural pigmentation during processing and, to retain their appetite appeal, are dyed with an artificial colourant. Indeed, some brands of processed peas achieve a synthetic blue-greenness that exceeds our wildest colour expectations!

Our demand for perfection and visual freshness causes the excessive bleaching and refining of many foodstuffs such as salt, sugar, rice and white flour and this processing is often at the expense of both flavour and nutrition.

Many additives control contamination, for instance mould inhibitors in bread, and bacteria inhibitors in red meats. However, much red meat achieves its pinky-redness from colour enhancers. To tempt us further, many butchers display meat on traditional white trays under the warm glow of red-biased lights emphasising its freshness and tenderness. In order to check this

illusion of a heightened redness, remove a cut from the freezer display and look at its appearance in daylight or under the shop lights.

Our conditioned attitudes to the colour of fresh food are slowly being re-educated. Inroads have been made as a result of campaigns for 'real food', for hormone-free meat, for organically farmed produce and for more information on additives and nutritional content. Moreover, full membership of the European Economic Community will bring further legislation that will restrict the use of artificial colourants and enhancers. By the mid-nineties the colour appearance of canned peas may be a more natural greenish-grey, kippers may lose their artificial golden skins and meat may look less pinky-red.

So much of flavour is governed by our colour expectation that appropriate hue and colour consistency is of prime concern in the mass marketing of food and vegetables.

Colour and taste

From the blue salt wrapper found in the earliest crisp packets, blues and blue-greens have been associated with sharp and acerbic tastes. These wrappers use similar colours and hue combinations to represent a salt and vinegar flavour.

The connection between vision and taste is a powerful one (see pages 32–3). Tests with blue-dyed mashed potatoes show that when the colour of a familiar food is radically altered the eater can become upset and even nauseated. Also, with vision removed, blindfolded people experience great difficulty identifying different drinks, such as sherry and brandy, and smokers cannot distinguish their brand from any other.

Tests have shown that we can easily be misled when the familiar colours of soft drinks, which rely upon colour for their flavour, have been altered. This colour-taste confusion was also high-

lighted in an experiment in which the hues and flavours of sherbets were mismatched. When the sherbets were white and made with any of the six test flavours – lemon, lime, orange, grape, pineapple and almond – the panel was confused and mostly unsuccessful in identifying individual flavours. Moreover, when the sherbets were deceptively coloured, the majority mistakenly identified the flavours. For example, when lime-coloured sherbet was served green, three quarters of the judges said that it was lime, but when it was coloured purple (as for grape), less than half identified it correctly.

This association of colour with other sensory properties is a phenomenon called 'synaesthesia' and it plays a key role in marketing. It occurs whenever our exposure to colour produces more than one stimulation, that is, when we cross-reference the visual sense with other senses. We find this colour phenomenon applied to packaging for instance, when a bottle of kitchen cleanser is coloured a pale yellow to suggest a lemon fragrance, or when a sweet is coloured red to enhance a cherry flavour.

One test (illustrated opposite) attempts to design colour schemes for packaging using three hues chosen to

communicate specific tastes. The first scheme (A) represents a tart, acid, citrous flavour. See if you can identify the others (the answers are in the caption).

Our attitude to the colours of taste and their suitability to different products varies between types of product. A German market research project examined the taste and efficiency of different toothpastes. Each tube of toothpaste was coloured grey and was marked respectively with a green, yellow and blue circle. The results showed that the preference given to one toothpaste or another depended largely upon the colour of the circular marking. The toothpaste in the tube marked blue achieved by far the

Which taste sensation do you think of when looking at each of these colour combinations?

A Acid; B Sweet; C Bitter; D Salted; E Liqueur-like, sweetish

highest score, blue being associated with freshness. To a lesser extent, freshness was also associated with the yellow tube but this attribute was never associated with the tube marked green. In a second version of the test, each flavour of toothpaste was presented in a different tube carrying one of the other three colours used in the test. Remarkably, the results remained exactly the same!

From these studies it can be seen that colour far outweighs flavour in the synaesthetic impression it makes on us. Colour powerfully influences not only our ability to identify a flavour, but it can also affect our estimation of a product's strength and quality.

Colour and quality

The publication of Vance Packard's book *Hidden Persuaders* in 1962 alerted an unsuspecting public to the concealed powers of psychological selling. We learned about the association of greenness and 'mountain stream' freshness in the successful marketing of menthol cigarettes and how poor selling California prunes, when tinned in yellow coloured cans, successfully switched their previous association with old, wrinkled skin to that of the health-giving properties of sun.

Recent market research consistently reinforces the point that the consumer not only judges the quality of a product by its colour appearance but that the

The colour of a product and, indeed, its packaging can also determine our judgement of its strength. For example, cleansing products like these that claim to be kind and gentle on the face and hands tend to be identified in pink.

colour of its wrapper is psychologically transferred to the strength and performance of the contained product. For example, when a handcream was market-researched in a pink version and in a white version, people consistently judged the pink cream to be milder.

This association of redness with mildness in cosmetics is reversed when in the context of tobacco products. A strong red is a common choice for the packaging of full-strength cigarettes, with milder blends being packaged in diluted greens, blues and purples.

These kinds of subjective judgements apply to all kinds of consumer goods where a customer will judge the quality of a product by the colour of its wrapper. This even applies to cars where young and young-in-heart drivers believe that a red sports car will out-perform those in other colours – a belief anticipated by some insurance companies who demand higher premiums for red coloured models.

Black is another high-speed colour for cars and one which is associated with VIPs and high status. Black clothes can bring a touch of class and black is also used to denote exclusivity in expensive goods such as designer furniture and high-tech electronics.

This direct relationship between the quality of a product and the colour of its container is again demonstrated by an American test in which 200 women were invited to judge the flavour of a coffee served from brown, red, blue and yellow coffee pots. Although the same coffee was served in each case, almost three quarters of those tested found the coffee from the brown pot to be too strong, whereas nearly half of the women found the coffee from the red pot to be rich and full-bodied. The coffee from the blue pot was regarded as having a milder aroma, while that from the yellow pot was judged to be made from a weaker blend of bean.

Therefore, it comes as no surprise to learn of another test in which the same new washing powder packaged in yellow,

Products claiming the strength to clean clothes and kill germs are packaged in highly saturated and dramatically contrasted power colours – the greater the strength of colour and contrast, the greater the implied power.

blue and a combination of yellow and blue drew quite different ratings. The detergent in the yellow box was reported as too strong. Indeed, it was said to have damaged fabrics. The powder in the blue pack was judged too weak to clean the wash, but the blue and yellow coloured pack and its powder was found to be 'marvellous' and 'very effective'.

Such market research provides two kinds of information. On the one hand, we begin to appreciate the enormous power of colour and the guile of merchandisers in channelling this power. On the other hand, we also begin to realise the depth of our own gullibility!

A corporate spectrum

Many companies not only use a colour psychology to advertise, package and mass market their products or services but have also directly linked their own company with a particular hue. For example, within a rainbow of product colours we find a corporate spectrum containing 'Harrod's Green', 'Kodak Yellow' and 'Sainsbury's Orange'.

Red is the appetite hue. It addresses our need for instant satisfaction. On fields of white it is the livery of Campbell's soups, Coca-Cola and Marlboro cigarettes. With yellow it is the colour of fast food and quick service and is synonymous with McDonald's, Wendy's, Wimpy's and the Royal Mail. When red turns pink it signifies femininity and the softness of second skin products like Camay and Oil of Ulay. When red becomes burgundy it denotes the elegant luxury of expensive perfumes and Dunhill cigarettes.

Orange is a power colour – the stronger the orange the greater its potency. Its vigour encompasses oven cleaners, health foods and protein packed snacks. It is the colour of Radion and also the colour of Lucozade, the latter beginning its life as a health drink but later, complete with its 'medicinal' orange wrapping, evolving into a popular soft drink.

Yellow, when golden, brings a long life to Duracell batteries and a touch of class to Schweppes tonic water. With a dash of red a stronger yellow is synonymous with Kodak film and Shell petroleum. On the former, yellow symbolises sunlight, the medium of photography; on the latter it evokes sunsets and the power to cross distant horizons.

Green is the safe alternative. Fuji film has successfully identified with green, as have Habitat, British Petroleum and the ubiquitous Pentel ballpoint. Green is also the colour of money. When American Express first launched their credit card it

appeared in an unsuccessful pale yellow. It was only when they switched to the colour of the dollar that it succeeded. Green addresses the destruction of the ozone layer and the growth of toxic waste. It is the hue of the Green Movement, of unleaded petrol and, together with blue and blue-grey, is emblematic of bio-degradable and ecologically sensitive products such as Ecover and Ark.

Green-Blue is the colour of consistency and is the hue of Barclay's Bank and Heinz Baked Beans. With red and white it gives packaged pasta a strong Italian flavour.

Blue represents reliability and is widespread in the world of banking, being used by the Midland Bank, Chase Man-

The corporate and product rainbow

hattan and Citicorp. Blue is also a common colour of air travel. It is prominent in the livery of Eastern Airlines and Pan Am and, with a touch of red and white, allows British Airways and Air France to fly their respective flags. Blue is also institutional and a safe investment. It colours the insignias and logos of many insurance companies and international corporations such as ICI, Ford, and General Motors.

Purple is the colour of forbidden fruit but it is also naughty but nice! Its association with smoothness and excitement links it to Cadbury's chocolates, Silk Cut cigarettes and exotic cocktails.

Colour preference

Colour preference test

Take a look at these colours. Which colour do you like best? Which colour do you like second best? Continue choosing colours until you have completed your personal order of preference.

Tests like this have been carried out by researchers in order to determine our liking and disliking of colours. However, many of these tests have, like the one you have just done, simply presented a range of painted colour samples and invited the viewer to arrange them in a preferred sequence. The most famous of all colour surveys was conducted in 1941 by Hans Eysenck. He simply collected together all the previous colour preference tests and amalgamated their findings into one overall order. He then published the order calling it the 'universal order of colour'. See if your colour selection agrees with Eysenck's finding. His 'universal order' was: 1 Blue; 2 Red; 3 Green; 4 Purple; 5 Yellow; 6 Orange.

Another colour preference survey carried out in 1977 (Porter) found a similar order to that of Eysenck. This set out to survey colour preference in different age groups. It found that Eysenck's 'universal order' was strongest in those people less affected by fashion colour trends, such as old people. It also found that the 'universal order' is formed around puberty when, as other studies have detected, we replace a preference for red with a preference for blue. The survey concluded that Eysenck's colour order represented an underlying and constant preference but that this could be altered from time to time by the influence of fashionable colour trends.

However, the main problem with such tests is that, by basing judgements on painted chips of paper, colour is removed from reality. Also, many tests take no account of the effect of shape or, indeed, of the effect of the colour dimensions of saturation and lightness.

One colour preference test in the late 1970s studied colour choices in relation to sweets. Children were invited to eat Smarties in their favourite order of preference. Rowntree-Mackintosh had supplied an especially colour coated range which comprised the hues used in Eysenck's test, but this time the dimensions of saturation and lightness were held constant, leaving only hue to signify the difference between the Smarties. The test assortment included a blue Smartie that was not included in the commercial range at that time. Regardless of hue, all the Smarties had the same flavour (commercial Smarties offer three flavours). Despite their past experience of

Smarties and of their flavours, the children placed blue as their unprecedented first choice.

This choice was interesting because, not only did it confirm Eysenck's position of blue in first place, it also challenged our known aversion to blue foodstuffs. Moreover, the popularity of the blue Smartie also reflects our connection of shape with colour. According to the research of Faber Birren in America, blue is associatd with circles, and Smarties are circular in shape. What is even more interesting is the fact that Rowntree-Mackintosh introduced an official and synthetic blue into their range in the 1980s!

The preference for blue crops up in a recent survey by *The Public Pulse*, the newsletter of the American Roper Organisation, where almost 50 per cent of those tested named it as their favourite colour with red in second place. Blue is America's top selling car colour with a red car in second place. Meanwhile, Britain's largest motor manufacturer names white as the top selling car colour with red in second and blue in third place.

Although Eysenck's first place blue and second place red feature consistently in colour surveys, our basic preference for these hues can be dislodged by our search for new and novel colour experience. This need is fed by the ever-changing cycles of colour in fashion which promote trends in all types of products.

The successful introduction of the blue Smartie provides a novelty that overrides our inherent dislike of this hue with things that we eat.

Forecasting colour trends

Many industries such as clothing, beauty and cosmetics, and soft furnishings depend heavily upon our constantly changing colour tastes for their existence. Indeed, their success in the marketplace hinges upon the accurate forecasting of tomorrow's trend setting colours.

Seasonal forecasts produced by the International Wool Secretariat for 1990–91 colour trends in women's fashion.

For this purpose they seek the guidance of groups and individuals who specialise in forecasting up and coming trends in their particular area of the market. This information is crucial as, in some cases, colours have to be determined up to two or three seasons ahead. For instance, the time lapse between the moment a colour selection is made and when a dress reaches the shop can be around 20 months. However, in the case of environmental goods such as cars, motorbikes, furniture etc, the time lapse can be several years.

To service this need each branch of industry holds its own international fair which draws together colour predictions from a variety of sources. One such fair is Premiere Vision held annually in Paris. This addresses the textile industry and acts as a crystal ball in which future colour trends are formulated from consultations between European forecasters. Once determined, the colours are then displayed on large presentation boards in the Hall of Prediction.

Similar consultations between experts in different fields occur all over the world. In England there is the Colour Group affiliated to the Chartered Society of Designers and closely associated with the Colour Marketing Group of America. Members of these forecasting agencies employ a variety of techniques. At the grass roots level, predicting colour trends can involve a daily assessment of all the subtle factors that might contribute to a new colour fashion. For example, this can include analysis of recurrent hues appearing in design magazines, of colours associated with successful museum exhibitions, or with box office successes at the cinema. The process also involves studying trends at street level. For instance, fashion predictor Sally Forbes regularly visits Camden Market to observe any new colour trends that might be developing at street level. These observations are fed into a system of prediction that may ultimately express itself as the colour fashion of tomorrow.

Jean Philippe Lenclos has analysed colour trends internationally and across different countries. He observes that during the 1970s colour cycles moved at different speeds for different industries. For example, fashion colours for clothes in 1975 were about two years ahead of those for the home. However, by 1976 colour trends had unified. This fusion of colour cycles has been endorsed more recently by the American colour consultant Leigh Rudd Simpson. In 1989 she confirmed that colour trends are driven by clothes fashion and added, 'When a colour comes into fashion and is accepted by the consumer, they respond by wanting to see that colour all around them – in interiors, cars, graphic design, etc.'

The pastel craze

One of the colour success stories of the 1980s has been the fashion for pastel hues. First launched to appeal to an upmarket and sophisticated consumer, the craze spread quickly and became associated with 'lifestyle'. The concept of lifestyle sees groups of colours being aimed at various attitudes or fantasies of living such as 'natural', 'sporty', 'classic', 'high-tech' and 'ethnic'. Colour ranges are then coordinated across all products associated with a particular 'style of living', from clothes to cars and from interiors to luggage.

Fed by popular television programmes like *Miami Vice*, the pastel trend became truly international in spirit. For example, the coordinated colours of men's and women's clothing in New York in 1985 appeared in the same year and in the same colours for new car models launched at the Frankfurt, Paris and Tokyo Motor Shows. Colours hitherto considered suitable only for baby clothes were worn by adults and were even used on Parker fountain pens and aggressive machines such as Honda motorbikes.

In America, designers painted the façades and interiors of their buildings in pastel shades and associated them with a new environmental design movement that rejected the grey drabness of a modernist architecture. The Japanese electronics industry launched pastel pink television sets and telephone handsets as well as soft grey transistor radios and steam irons highlighted in pale yellow, blue and pink.

Pastel colours invaded Britain's high streets and appeared to hallmark the shortlived consumer boom of the late eighties. This trend still lingers with many stores, such as Dorothy Perkins, DER Rentals and Virgin Records, which sport pastels as part of their shop signs. The early part of the craze saw the success of ICI's Natural Whites, a range of white paint tinted with a hint of colour (see page 54). The pastel period also saw

BELOW AND RIGHT:

During the pastel craze in the mid-eighties, colour combinations hitherto considered suitable only for baby clothes became fashionable in men's co-ordinates and even extended to aggressive machines such as this Honda opposite.

the rise of 'muffin', a soft beige pastel that became the best-selling paint (after white) of the decade.

Other colour trends have also been in evidence. The late eighties saw black, the relentless fashion colour, achieve renewed status. It was no longer just the colour of mourning and glamour but represented a supreme and mystical elegance in many forms of design. With metallics, black also addressed our high-tech and futuristic fantasies; with neutrals it reflected our fascination with an ethnic Japan. The ascendancy of an 'environmental' colour range led by green, terracotta, soft brown and antique gold has now become a reality. In echoing new attitudes to the state of our planet, these colours take us into the future.

Colour and novelty

At various times throughout history a developing colour technology has produced brilliant new hues. One such point came in the 1860s when William Henry Perkin launched his new analine-based mauve dye on a Victorian world. Quickly joined by a strong and synthetic red, as well as purple and green dyes, mauve not only caused a sensation in women's clothing at the time but it also gave its name to what became known as the 'Mauve Decade' (see page 69).

In the 1930s, Schiaparelli stunned the fashion world with her Shocking Pink – a hue that was to regain novelty value in the 1950s as Lipstick Pink. Again, in the 1970s, Kinky Pink, a near fluorescent paint, became fashionable on interior walls of the time.

Even in the colour saturated world of today we are still bedazzled by new colour experiences. Our search for novelty has seen the blue Smartie, the return of the 'banned' red M&M sweets, the multi-coloured Swatch wristwatch and even the colourisation of black and white Hollywood film classics. Our recent fascination with surface colour dazzle has pointed to a future technology in the iridescent holograms on our credit cards. It has also returned to the past in the revival of traditional decorating

April Love *by Arthur Hughes, 1856.*

techniques for creating a three-dimensional illusion on the surface of walls using sponging and stippling. The surface novelty of colour has now extended from the metallised paints on our cars to pearlised plastics. Eagerly adopted for packaging by the beauty industry, pearlised plastic is now available in every colour of the rainbow.

Meanwhile, an advancing technology constantly seeks new ways to catch our attention. The future holds the promise of opalescent paints, of materials that will change hue in response to body heat, and a glass that will change colour on command. This latter innovation will, in a sense, allow us to change the colour of

William Perkins' discovery of an analine purple dye became the novelty fashion colour of the mid-nineteenth century. Today, startling mismatches of colour and form are much used in art and advertising. This ad uses 'colour shock' to both draw attention to the novelty of a pink shark and also promote a new colour range for plastics.

our world at an instant and will affect everything from windscreens to ski goggles.

In advertising, the search for colour novelty has seen a new twist. Many adverts, such as ICI's pink shark advert, now portray familiar objects in the novelty of the 'wrong' colour. To grab our attention, some television and magazine adverts have returned to the novelty of black and white against which only the product is seen in full colour. First used in pop videos, this novel technique mirrors the film *The Wizard of Oz* where black and white represented reality and Technicolor symbolised the land of dreams.

GREAT PINK

CONCLUSION

We cannot ignore colour. Technology has filled our modern world with more colours than ever before thought possible. Colour affects our lives on so many levels and, as consumers, we are literally bombarded with colour from magazines, from shop windows, and from all branches of the media. Each time we buy a packet of sweets, select a dress or a tie or decorate a room we are confronted with colour decisions. Some of our decisions are made intuitively, i.e. influenced by our preference, while others are based on fashion or on a whim. We have attempted to inform these decisions by presenting colour, not as a decorative element, but as a powerful means of expressing our mood and personality. The communication power of colour is as complex a language as is our use of words and music.

INDEX